THE DRIVE
TO ELECTRIC

HOW INNOVATIVE MINDS
ARE SHAPING OUR FUTURE

DR. VERONIKA WRIGHT

THE DRIVE TO ELECTRIC
Table of Contents

THE DRIVE TO ELECTRIC

Our world is currently experiencing a transformation in transportation similar to the one that took place at the beginning of the 20th century. At that time, the main means of transportation in many parts of the world changed from horses and carriages to automobiles. This transition produced some of the largest companies in the world, such as Ford, General Motors, Volkswagen, and Toyota. Despite the greatest cultural and social upheavals, world wars, the oil crisis and other disruptive events, the industry continues to thrive today. But we can see that the landscape is changing. An electric transformation is taking place.

In this E-transformation, "The Drive to Electric", we are converting our transportation system from gas- and diesel-powered vehicles to battery- and fuel cell-powered alternatives. In the best case, we realize the full potential of this transition by combining it with green energy generation. Instead of using oil, coal, or gas to generate electricity, we use solar, wind or hydro power. Since these renewable energy sources are often available sporadically, we store the energy in batteries so it can be called up when needed. The E-transformation, which has dramatically picked up speed from 2021, means that traditionally separate markets such as energy generation, storage and use will suddenly be connected - by a battery.

I grew up in the green heart of Austria and my family instilled in me values such as respect for nature, the environment, and every individual in our society. After my studies in Technical Physics and my PhD in Quantum Mechanics, I've been fortunate to work in the automotive industry on technologies that enable this E-transformation. I have been involved with electric vehicles, batteries, electric motors, and inverters - all around the globe. When I decided to move to the US and start my own company in the area of battery technologies, it didn't take long to find so many inspirational people already involved in changing this world for the better, driving this E-transformation. After a few conversations with some of them, I wanted to share these amazing stories.

Follow along as I talk with these inspiring thought leaders about their life stories and their passion for the global drive to electric we are experiencing right now. In this day and age where the hype around technology dominates all the headlines, it is increasingly important to understand what is real. Let's listen to the experts, hear their views, and learn from them. They are comprised of university professors to startup founders to industry leaders from around the world. India, North America, Canada, Russia, Europe, or Singapore. How did they find their way into the world of batteries and electrification? Why are they working on these technologies? What is their vision for our electrified future? What challenges do they face? What can we learn from their lives?

For me, the backbone of this whole journey is the battery. The battery is something everyone is familiar with, we all use it every day but probably don't give too much thought to where it comes from, how it is used, and what happens when it is "dead". This is important for all batteries, from small hearing aid batteries to very large batteries like those used in electric vehicles. To understand this complete picture, I would like to share with you what I call "The Battery Biography – The Life of a Battery".

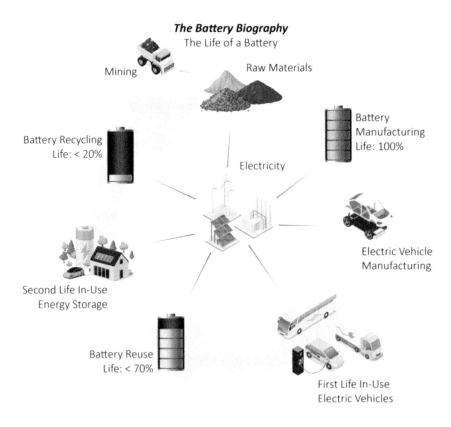

The Battery Biography
The Life of a Battery

Mining

Raw Materials

Battery Manufacturing
Life: 100%

Battery Recycling
Life: < 20%

Electricity

Electric Vehicle
Manufacturing

Second Life In-Use
Energy Storage

Battery Reuse
Life: < 70%

First Life In-Use
Electric Vehicles

Basically, the battery biography records and tells the complete story of the battery through its entire life – from birth to rebirth to reincarnation. The best way to explain this is with an example. Since everybody knows what an electric vehicle is, let's take an electric vehicle car battery through the battery biography. The first step is mining raw materials. These materials are used by battery manufacturers to make a battery. The auto manufacturer then puts this battery to use in its first life, an electric vehicle. From there, the electric vehicle is driven for many years, charged, and discharged until it reaches its end of first life. Once it is determined that the battery is no longer viable for an electric vehicle, we can take it and repurpose it for another less demanding application, like an energy storage system. Finally, we recycle the battery to get back the raw materials and the process begins again.

However, the determination of repurpose or recycle greatly depends on its previous life which is why the battery biography, and the recording of its life is so important.

All the people and companies in this book are involved in the battery biography in some way, be it in one of the core areas or in the bridges we build between them. I was inspired by every conversation. While I am generally an open-minded person, I cannot see all the challenges and opportunities on my own. I need other people with different backgrounds and opinions to give me a broader perspective. And this is what I want to share.

This book aims to inspire you. It offers expert opinions from thought leaders, their careers, and their vision - their WHY, in a field and market that is growing with an enormous speed. You'll gain a fundamental understanding of the battery's role throughout its lifecycle, from electric vehicles to energy storage to recycling. You will learn why we need to move away from the traditional linear economy to form a circular one, where resources are led in a circle. It may get a bit technical in places, but I've tried to keep this to a minimum, so hang in there. However, if you are expecting a PhD thesis on battery technologies and recycling methods, this is not the book for you. At best, I hope you leave with much curiosity and the urge to learn more about our drive to electric. Because we are all part of making this movement successful.

Enjoy!

#EV Electrified Veronika

Expertise, Empathy, Enthusiasm

E-WASTE AND BATTERY REUSE

Almost every animal behaves responsibly
in the forest to turn someone's waste into value.
It's shameful for us as humans not to do that.

DARSHAN VIRUPAKSHA

May 29th, 2021, India

CHAPTER 01
E-WASTE AND BATTERY REUSE

O ur world today is rightfully called a consumer market - we consume everything from food to entertainment, and also electronics. We use our electronics, like computers, entertainment systems, or smartphones, and then when the next best thing comes along, we get rid of the old one. We probably don't think too much about where they go after we get rid of them. Are they still good? Maybe some of them are good enough for something else, but in this day and age it's just easier to throw them away.

To begin I would like you to meet Darshan Virupaksha, co-founder of a startup company called Nunam.

Darshan was bothered by the "throw-away mindset" of our society at a very early age, which motivated him to find alternatives to this way of thinking. Growing up in India, he witnessed the E-revolution and was concerned about the amount of electronic waste that would be generated over the next decades. Along with his co-founder, he began a journey to enable the **Reuse of Batteries** in a second life. An electric vehicle battery is considered "dead" when it typically still has two thirds of its life left. It's just not suitable for use in a car any longer. Darshan saw this and realized that there would be a huge potential market of dead electric vehicle batteries that could still have a whole second life powering something else.

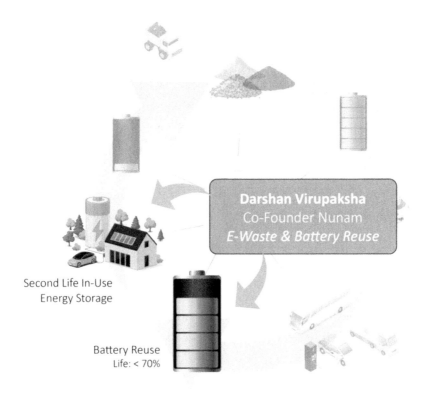

Darshan Virupaksha
Co-Founder Nunam
E-Waste & Battery Reuse

Second Life In-Use
Energy Storage

Battery Reuse
Life: < 70%

After talking with Darshan during our interview, I really understand what kind of person he is and why it matters where he comes from to understand what drives him and his strong messages for our society. Darshan is truly a change maker. Of his yearly 52 weekends, he spends 50 of those working on projects related to IoT (Internet of Things), health, electrification, and energy. Having grown up in India and witnessing the IT and energy revolution, all he ever wanted and wants to do is help. *"It's not about making money. It's about changing people's lives. If it can touch millions of people, I never thought about it twice. I just do it."*

Darshan Virupaksha is the co-founder of a startup called Nunam, based in Bengaluru, India. "Nunam" is Sanskrit (Indian) and means "created for the future". Nunam's vision is to provide electricity for rural areas by giving used batteries a second life. Thereby turning somebody's electronic waste into value for people who need it the most. *"We do this primarily for those communities who need affordable energy the most and live with less or no access to electricity today."*

It all started with a little weekend project. *"We tested 400 old battery cells from laptops and smart phones and found that two thirds of them were still good."* This may come as a surprise to most of you, but in fact, about 80% of the laptop and smartphone batteries we consumers throw away as electronic waste are still functional and still providing power. In the automotive market for the case of electric cars it is even more surprisingly wasteful. Lithium-ion batteries in electric cars are called "dead" when they still have two-thirds of their energy left. They still function and they still have the capability to store energy and deliver energy on demand, but they are simply no longer good enough for an electric car.

Darshan wondered what happens to all those used batteries when they reach the end of their lives? What happens to all the electronic waste that our society produces? Who is responsible for the battery waste? Does this waste have any value? Is it even "waste"?

To answer these questions, Darshan and his co-founder Prodip Chatterjee relied not on Bloomberg reports, but on their own research and test data. Taking a practical approach and drawing on academic research and do-it-yourself projects from the Internet, they concluded fairly quickly: *"We realized that at this energy growth rate, if there was no way to build economics for reverse logistics of electronic waste and recycling, it would be a massive problem. It would be all about how plastic is today. We studied the supply chain, investigated the volume of E-waste which will get accumulated over the next years and we saw that if there is no money put in from used batteries, consumers to recycling, batteries will end up in landfills."*

Darshan speaks very authentically, and you can feel his whole heart and enthusiasm for everything he does. He was born in Bangalore, which is now considered the fastest growing startup ecosystem in India - the Silicon Valley of India. The city has a solid legacy of cutting-edge R&D

labs, academic institutions, and public companies, and has contributed significantly to India's leadership in IT.

When Darshan was growing up in the 1990s, Bangalore was not as vibrant as it is today. Visits to his relatives always included a ride on a horse cart from the train station to their house. Suddenly the IT revolution took hold: *"In the '90s, money started flowing into the country - India never had 3G, they switched from 2G to 4G."* He laughs heartily and says, *"I know it sounds like I'm 100 years old, but the spectrum of change was really visible to me as I grew up."* When he was young, he watched these geopolitical changes that were happening so quickly and recognized the increasing challenge this country would face in the energy sector in the future. All these changes during this IT revolution would require huge demands of electronics and energy. Back then, Darshan was thinking *"We're not moving! Why aren't we moving? That was always going through my mind."*

Well, Darshan himself is someone who moves. And he moves quickly and decisively! *"A lot of who I am today goes back to my grandfather, who always inspired curiosity in me."* Together, they had worked on small projects and scientific programs where Darshan developed his ability to tinker and his "JUST TRY" and "DO IT" mentality. Since then, he has wanted to create things, *"to take something abstract and make something real out of it. I always need paper and real-world stuff."* This reminds me of my own dad who, when he wanted to help me with my math or physics homework after school, would always tell me to grab a pen and paper and make a drawing first. I still always need my pen and paper.

Darshan's curiosity runs through his entire life. Darshan has never worked for a big company, and he has a clear opinion about it: *"If I worked for a big company, this would never have happened - I never want to work for a big company!"* Since he finished school, he has been working with several startups on a variety of innovative ideas - on workdays and on especially on weekends. He basically puts his whole life into it. The common thread in his projects and ideas is finding a solution to a socio-economic problem using technology. Darshan puts solving human problems and helping others over personal bragging or generating millions. When he observed problems as he grew up, he always strove for solutions.

"*We built Alexa back in 2013 even before Amazon came out with it,*" Darshan describes full of excitement. "*Our virtual assistant technology was just like Amazon Alexa which is capable of voice interaction to control smart devices. We called it Alex. We had a whole demonstration, but it had nothing to do with Amazon. We said, Alex, turn on the TV. Alex, turn off the lights. IoT was pretty new back then. This was my personal start into connected ecosystems. I understood challenges of generating data, transferring to the cloud, processing it, and how to make it techno-commercially feasible.*" This was the foundation of a lot of his later activities in the battery industry.

In 2017, a lucky coincidence finally brought him to the world of batteries. Through a Facebook post, Darshan met his future co-founder Prodip Chatterjee. "*It's a strange story with a lot of unexpected things.*" Prodip grew up in Germany and lives in Berlin. He also has Indian roots. When he visited his family during his holiday travels, he began to see this energy problem in person, tons of hazardous E-waste, underutilized batteries, and a lack of clean energy. "*Prodip was the catalyst. He saw the energy problem. We didn't aim to form a company; we just started a project. We bought some old batteries on the market to see if we could reuse them. I did that after work and on weekends. We built a prototype in a couple of months. We wanted to see if it was possible to reuse old batteries and create something new. Prodip did some research and shared some links, and I wanted to get things going and try it out myself.*"

What started as a little side project turned into a real company, Nunam, literally "created for the future". Nunam collects batteries that the "first consumer" no longer needs and gives them a second life. They build energy storage devices from used lithium-ion batteries for those who need affordable energy the most. Prodip is the second half of a battery biography with another who cares deeply about extending the life of an old battery. Whether these are lithium-ion batteries for laptops and smartphones or large car batteries, Nunam eagerly collects them and puts them to new use. "*Once we hand out refurbished batteries, we also take care that these batteries come back to us, and we send them to recyclers. First, we source used batteries, then dismantle them, characterize them, remanufacture them, track their performance in their second life, and then finally send them to the recycler.*"

This way, Nunam ensures that after their second life, all batteries are brought to a recycling center to recover the valuable raw materials that batteries are made of. These batteries will not end up in landfills, because they are tracked over their second lifetime and Nunam makes itself responsible to bring them to a recycler. Most people are surprised when they hear how much of these valuable raw materials, such as cobalt, nickel, lithium, and others, can be recovered and made into new battery material through a recycling process. There is more about this later in the book.

With a warm tone and a certain proud enthusiasm, Darshan enumerates other second life projects he has initiated with Nunam. "*We built an energy storage system for a tribe living in the forest. One day there was a wedding, and they had no electricity. With our system made of used batteries, they were able to continue the wedding. We really created a memory for this village.*" Another project assists forest watchers who struggle with flashlights that didn't last more than two to three hours, making it difficult for them to return to the camp. Nunam designed a handy flashlight that runs on used lithium-ion batteries and can be carried in a pocket. This enables forest watchers to safely return to their camps every night.

What was the biggest challenge for you and Nunam?

"*We decided to take on this challenge because it would have an impact on developing countries. We started applying for funds. We wrote hundreds of applications. It took several months but no one wanted to fund our idea. They only funded products that are market ready."* After several traditional failing funding rounds, they changed their strategy and reached out to laptop and car manufacturers directly. They finally connected with the Audi Environmental Foundation- Audi AG's daughter organization- and began a collaboration. *"That was an important milestone for us."*

The collaboration between Nunam and Audi is about building solar nanogrids from the used electric vehicle batteries out of the all-electric Audi e-tron cars. A solar grid is a local and self-sufficient energy system that includes power generation by solar cells and energy storage by batteries. It generates electricity without being part of the public grid infrastructure. In this way, Nunam is creating a way to supplement power supply in India with second life energy storage systems, especially in rural areas. These nanogrids keep everyday items such as lamps working for shopkeepers and artisans in India. Nunam's customers describe themselves as the generation of solar energy entrepreneurs who are finding a faster, cleaner, and more economical path to universal access to electricity. While the collaboration between Nunam and Audi currently involves the reuse of batteries from Audi prototypes and test vehicles, the next step would be to apply the same concept to the reuse of batteries that have reached the end of their useful life in electric cars on the road.

Audi and Nunam are not the only ones looking at the possibility of reusing batteries after automotive life. A few more have popped up in recent years. Nissan is using old car batteries to power small robots, VW is building portable charging stations, and Renault is building stationary energy storage systems from used car batteries. Other automakers such as BMW, Proterra, and Lucid Motors have incorporated reuse principles into their battery designs from the beginning. Audi even uses some of its used batteries for forklifts and VW is using some for portable charging stations.

What is the technological challenge to enable battery reusability?

"For most of the companies in the battery industry, the battery is more or less a black box. There is a lot of secrecy. Many of the stakeholders in the battery value chain just want to hold all the information to themselves, but nobody knows exactly what is valuable in a battery and what is not. This lack of clarity is creating a barrier, especially for making batteries reusable. We need a large momentum to break this barrier. There is no value to intellectual property if it is not generating anything. By sharing information, we generate value. Sure, this is happening more and more with various collaborations across the world, but it has to be ramped up as a culture! A culture where value chains become more efficient than isolated businesses making profits."

The accessibility of information and data during the life of a battery can be enabled by collaboration of key stakeholders. Companies that make batteries have to work together with companies that make electric vehicles, and they have to work together with companies that reuse and recycle the batteries. This is one of the key takeaways for this book. To understand the health of a used battery, you need to know what has happened to it during its entire life. Knowing the type of battery and how it was used can help determine whether the battery is reusable or needs to be recycled. Currently, the biggest challenge for companies reusing or recycling batteries is figuring out what type of battery they just received is and what condition it is in. Is it damaged? Has it been in an accident? Is it safe? What chemistry is it? How was it used? What happened to this battery? Darshan has a very strong and honest conclusion. *"This whole point of maintaining intellectual property and holding secrecy is killing reusability. If we can keep thinking about reuse at every point in time, things would be very different today. If we can push reuse at every stage from designing batteries to manufacturing, I would be very happy. There should be a constraint in design - it has to be reusable!"*

While Darshan promotes the business of battery reuse, he tries his best to actively integrate the idea of reuse and recycling into his daily lifestyle, both in his personal life and in his business. *"It is a challenge, but I try. I must admit, it is really hard to make all things sustainable at this moment. It starts with a toothbrush. A toothbrush is not reusable, by design."* He mentions other examples such as carpooling, not using plastic in the office, and composting food waste. *"Compost is a good example. We compost food waste in our office. It's a circular approach. Everyone participates in this, and everyone can replicate it at home. We do it step by step. Eliminating plastic in the office is not possible right now. The reality is challenging, but we shouldn't lose hope! Reuse is unfortunately considered to be uncool, but we need to change that on a long term. You are often times looked down on when you want to reuse a car. In fact, many used cars leave their original countries and end in developing countries."*

If we think about the status of reusing products in general, reusing clothes and food, using other people's products second hand, does not have a high value in many parts of the world. Darshan refers to a school project Nunam is undertaking to encourage our children and their families to reuse products. *"We create battery power banks made of used batteries and use this as a tool to get the kids used to REUSE. Reuse is cool and makes sense. In some areas you are respected if you reuse. The ancient part of our culture did it very well. Every element in the house was reused. Just in today's modern society it is different."*

Listening to Darshan and his visionary and positive mindset excites me. Being in this industry myself, I know that there are many technical and economic challenges for a company like Nunam. Reusing batteries that are still good enough makes a lot of sense for the environment. But for many countries, this is not economically feasible at this time. Given the expense of dismantling and remanufacturing, making new battery controls and communications, and building a new product from battery technology that might be more than eight years old makes it not viable. In addition, there is always new competition from newer and cheaper battery technologies at the time of reuse so it is questionable whether this can be a financially positive business. With the increasing importance of direct recycling and the lack of accessible raw materials, there also seems to be a pressure to recover these raw materials as quickly as possible. On the other hand, reusing batteries in second life applications could significantly reduce battery electric vehicle prices because of the additional value stream coming from the second life consumers.

In spite of this, Darshan has big plans. He is envisioning battery repurposing centers all around the world. For every 2000 households you need one repurposing center. *"Just like garbage collection centers, we have battery repurposing centers. Not super fancy with X-ray, we need it affordable. We can't have 2-million-dollar machines to figure out the status of the battery. We have to make it lean enough and simplify the technology and the process."* He is emphasizing the importance of a battery ecosystem where companies are working together to make this happen. The next two to three years will be very critical for everybody who works in the battery reuse area. *"We don't control most of the battery value chain, but we need access to a majority of it to make reusability economically and technically feasible."*

"We can't solve all problems at the same time. If repurpose can help a part of our society in their everyday life, this will elevate them from poverty. By providing access to energy, you would solve the poverty challenge. Today's poverty is energy poverty. They need to be economically independent. Without access to affordable and efficient energy sources, the poor get poorer, and the socio-economic gap gets wider."

Listening to this 31-year-young man, I understand Nunam's larger vision. Unlock the true socio-economic and environmental potential of batteries. By providing technologies that give used batteries a second life. *"I feel privileged to be part of this period. We can be change makers!"*

If you were an animal, which one would it be? I ask Darshan as a final question in our interview. "*It's a tough choice*," he says and mentions the beaver building small dams in the stream. "*It uses local resources to create an opportunity for himself. I hope to survive with the same attitude. Just use what you have and make it happen!*"

HOW CHEMISTRY MATTERS FOR BATTERIES

You invent by thinking about what the end product is.
The end product has to be cheap!

Donald Sadoway
May 13th, 2021, USA

CHAPTER 02
HOW CHEMISTRY MATTERS
FOR BATTERIES

I magine starting from square one with the end goal to have a battery electric vehicle. There are two ways to find the right battery technology. You can use existing batteries from consumer electronics or other industrialized applications and try to scale them up to a vehicle size. Or you can work backwards to first understand the economic requirements and then find new technologies. Most of the industry has taken the first approach, which has brought the cost of electric vehicles down significantly in recent decades, but they are still too expensive compared to gas-powered cars. Professor Donald Sadoway decided to take the second route. He looked for technologies that would enable the desired price per kilowatt-hour and then solved the complicated problem of industrialization.

After looking at electronic waste and batteries from a second life perspective in the last chapter, here you will get an understanding about what needs to be considered to **Make a Battery**. This covers one of the most researched topics in the world today: battery technology. You will be surprised at how many different chemical makeups and shapes batteries can have. There is a whole battery zoo out there. Everyone is looking for the holy grail of long-lasting, safe, powerful, and inexpensive batteries.

The innovative thought leader representing this part of the battery value chain is a professor at MIT and co-founder of three companies. He entertains and teaches first time learners in such an inspiring way that the classroom isn't big enough to accommodate all the students who sign up for his chemistry class. At age 71, he has set his sights on developing new batteries for the energy storage and automotive markets. In his view, today's standard lithium-ion technology for electric cars is not sufficient and needs to be reinvented to become cheaper, safer, and more reliable.

Battery Manufacturing
Life: 100%

Donald Sadoway
Prof. MIT, Co-Founder Ambri
How Chemistry Matters for Batteries

I contacted Prof. Donald Sadoway on LinkedIn, a business platform that I use regularly to exchange with like-minded people, companies, and business partners. That day, by accident, I stumbled across a YouTube video on a channel called "Now You Know", where he was interviewed about liquid metal batteries. I was fascinated by his way of explaining this highly complex subject and thought he would be a perfect fit for my book. He answered my message the minute after I sent it. Our interview occurred virtually via Zoom. Prof. Sadoway joined the video call wearing a very elegant suit and a colorful tie.

Prof. Sadoway was born in Canada in the 1950s as a "*mid-century modern*", as he is calling himself. With his grandparent's roots in Ukraine, he grew up with an immigration background in a three-generation household with one younger brother in the then Anglo-Canadian part of the country. Thinking back about his time at school he remembers, "*In school I was the other guy. I worked really hard as a student. I realized that you need to be excellent because you are not part of the social power structure. You will not get a job because you are the son of someone.*" He enjoyed music and played hockey. He was the goalkeeper. "*Again, sort of the odd person. In a team, as a goalkeeper, you are the alone person. But you have a big responsibility. It doesn't matter what everybody else does - if you fail, the other team scores.*"

"*My grandparents and parents taught me to be socially conscientious. They needed to be very active in the community because they were a minority. We needed to stick together and give back to the community.*" With a warm tone in his voice, he says, "*I was taught to be a giver, not a taker. As part of the service piece, I was very much attracted to teaching.*"

He wanted to go to university to be able to come back as a teacher for the local school. "*I love languages, but if I go to university and study language classes, how will I make a living. I decided to go to the University of Toronto to study science and then come back as a science teacher.*" Of all the sciences, he was drawn to chemistry. "*I really liked chemistry because it was the least precise. Physics is very mathematical. You can throw a ball and calculate where it lands. Physics is very precise. In Chemistry you have some guard rails but there is lots of mystery, a lot that you just don't know. I was never afraid of being uncertain.*"

I can relate to that. When I did my PhD in physical chemistry, we had a mixed group of physicists and chemists in our research group. As a physicist, I always wanted to calculate everything based on the underlying laws and according to formulas. The chemist in our group had this natural gut feeling. She looked at the molecular structure and had a feeling - she was instinctively right.

Prof. Sadoway remembers about how he chose the field and topic for his undergraduate and doctoral studies: "*When I was doing my undergraduate degree, I chose my thesis topic based on the person, not the subject matter. I looked at all the faculties, and there was one professor who was doing high-temperature electrochemistry. He was from Greece, had done his PhD in London and then had come to Canada. I went with him. That was my introduction to high-temperature chemistry. If he had been a ceramist, I would have been a ceramist, too. Thank God he wasn't a ceramist.*"

Prof. Sadoway completed his doctorate in 1977. This was followed by an extraordinarily successful academic career in the fields of chemical metallurgy and batteries. After finishing his PhD at the University of Toronto he was awarded the NATO postdoctoral fellowship and moved to USA to start his postdoctoral research at MIT, Massachusetts Institute of Technology, in Boston. This academic career allowed him to follow his passion for education, which he noticed so early. He did not go back to his school in Canada, as he had originally planned, but became a professor at MIT. "*I've always been passionate about teaching.*" Prof. Sadoway taught several key classes at MIT and quickly earned an impressive reputation for teaching. Students were saying, "*this professor can explain things that are hard to understand and knows how to communicate with first-time learners.*"

To expedite student movement, he says, "*I play music at the beginning of each class.*"

In the fifteen minutes between classes, 450 people have to leave and enter the room. Prof. Sadoway uses this time to play music. "*I choose the music thematically linked to the subject I am teaching. If I am teaching about hydrogen bonding, I would play Handel's water music. I am teaching about polymers, I play Aretha Franklin – Chain, chain, chain. Sometimes I play music that I like, world music to inspire my students and expose them to things that I know.*" He teaches his classes by telling stories. "*We start with nothing. Nobody understands anything. There are just patterns.*" Then he starts including accomplished people and their stories – Nils Bohr finishes his PhD in Copenhagen and goes to England, where there is a conspiracy between J.J. Thomson and him, and he starts experimenting. *"It's about the people, the time, the setting, the place."* He emphasizes: *"This is not a chemistry class – this is a chemistry centered class. I love this class, it's a fantastic thing to teach."*

In the early 2000s there was an initiative by a group of electrical engineers at MIT. The students went to the professors with the proposal to allow open courses streamed on the internet, so everybody in the world could get access to MIT courses on the web for free. *"The internet in 2002 was getting the bandwidth to allow video streaming."* Some professors did not want to share their classes and, overall, the president thought this would be too radical at that time. *"In 2003, they put my chemistry class online."* The popularity of Prof. Sadoway's classes had increased so much, that the number of students wanting to take his class exceeded the number of seats in the auditorium. *"The majority of the students did not take chemistry from the chemistry department but from me. So, they wanted to record my lecture. There was a single camera that captured the room. My one-hour lecture would be streamed on MIT TV six times a day, even at midnight and then at 8pm, 9pm, 10pm, 11pm and 1am!"* He keeps smiling and says, *"The most heavily watched hour was the 1am!"* Prof. Sadoway looks at his own recordings each year before the new semester begins to reflect, improve the content, and make sure the freshmen, *"the first-time learners"* can understand all the stories he is telling.

There were two pivotal moments in his life that guided and initiated his work on batteries and electrification. *"In 1993 I was invited to give a lecture at a university. The subject, students should find ways to improve the air quality of Los Angeles. Some thought electric vehicles could be one possible approach. Nobody was teaching electrochemistry at that time. They asked me to come and lecture about batteries as well as emissions of aluminum compared to steel. I had to prepare for that myself because I didn't work on batteries at that time. I was surprised about all the stuff on batteries and how little progress we had made. Well, I gave my lecture and then a group of us was invited to Ford Motor Company in Michigan. While we were there, Ford showed us that they had an all-electric car. Back in 1993! They used a sodium sulfur battery, which was invented at Ford in 1963."*

The Ford Ecostar was developed as a two-door all electric delivery van using a sodium-sulfur battery developed by ABB Group in Germany. They had an experimental fleet of around 100 vans and were testing them for 30 months. To keep the sulfur in these batteries molten, they had to be operated at an elevated temperature of 600 °F (316 °C). During the testing period, two of the batteries caught fire - sulfur is flammable. Ford decided at that time to switch over to fuel cell electric vehicles and stopped this development. Around the same time, General Motors stopped their EV 1 program and the Argonne National laboratories abandoned it too. *"Gasoline was 25 cents a gallon. Nobody cared about electric cars."*

While the big automakers were stopping their battery efforts, Prof. Sadoway was expanding it.

"They let us test the electric car on the highway. That was fantastic! What they say about Tesla, that's nothing! I drove like that in 1993! I was so excited about this electric car. Believe me, it did not have anything to do with tail pipe emissions - I just loved the fact you have this incredible acceleration! I went back home, looked into the mirror, and told myself: The only reason we don't have electric cars on the road is the batteries. You are an electrochemist, what are you doing about it?" This one moment in 1993 driving this electric car inspired him to start working on batteries and electrification. *"I worked on metal production and batteries. I got involved with another faculty member and we invented the lithium polymer battery."*

The current state-of-the art technology for all-electric cars is lithium-ion batteries.

"Lithium-ion has been fantastic. It came to the world in the 1990s originally invented for mobile and handheld devices, such as phones and laptops. I think lithium-ion is ideal for small format, but then it became used in automotive. The bigger the format, the bigger the threat." Prof. Sadoway does not see lithium-ion technology as the appropriate technology for the global rollout of the electric car market. And even less so for grid-level storage, i.e. lithium-ion batteries for stationary energy storage systems to store electricity from renewable energy sources. There are two reasons for that. *"First, safety. I want a battery technology that is nonflammable, so we don't have a fire in case of a crash. And I don't want to see people justifying the electric vehicle fire by comparing it with the combustion engine vehicle fire. I want to make it safe!"* The second reason is cost. *"We don't see widespread deployment of electric vehicles because they are still too expensive. Why? Because of the battery. We are hitting a plateau with the current technologies. The average price of a new combustion engine car is $35.000. For somebody to change from combustion engine to electric vehicle, you need to give them something better and cheaper. Instead, it has less range and is more expensive."* With a certain determination he adds, *"For a widespread deployment I need a battery that is safer and cheaper. I am working on it. It's gunna be fantastic!"*

Prof. Sadoway has a clear vision of how his research addresses some of the technological challenges of modern lithium-ion battery technology, but also doesn't want to diminish the work and effort that industry and researchers have put into these technologies to date. *"All the hard work on lithium-ion battery technology is so important and valuable. It helps us to get started and get all the infrastructure in place. You just replace the battery with another technology, and it works! I can put a hamster on a wheel in there and the car doesn't care. The car will still drive. The car doesn't care where the electrons come from."*

The second pivotal moment in his life that led him even more into batteries was twelve years after his visit at Ford Motor Company. In 2005, during a workshop at the MIT about emissions in the energy sector, a man approached him. Prof. Sadoway remembers the conversation very well, *"This guy approached me and said 'You know, we have been looking at the big unsolved problems and one of them is grid level storage. Nobody has a clue about grid level storage. You have done all the work on electrometallurgy. Is there anything relevant to this? Can't we do something here?' and then he left my office. I started thinking about it."* Inspired by this conversation, Prof. Sadoway was starting to think about the process of producing aluminum from its raw material. This is called aluminum smelting. Aluminum smelting is the process of extracting aluminum from its oxide, the compound of aluminum and oxygen. It takes a tremendous amount of electrical power to break it apart. *"It runs 24 hours a day and seven days a week - drawing electricity, turning dirt into metal - for $1 per kilogram."* His voice raises enthusiastically, he is almost shouting with excitement, *"That's a modern miracle, an economic miracle. Now, here is a device that is big, traffic's huge amount of electricity and produces metal really cheap. What if I can teach this thing not to consume electricity but to store it and give it back on demand?"*

He started with the conceptualization of liquid metal batteries.

Liquid metal batteries consist of molten liquid metals and a salt electrolyte. To keep the metals molten, they operate at elevated temperatures. *"I conceptualized it myself. I never relied on anyone. I did not begin by going to the library and looking at everything that others had published. No, it was just what I taught my students. Where is the electro-negativity difference, where does it like to bond?"* He remembers a conversation with his former PhD supervisor. Prof. Sadoway had entered his office and his supervisor asked, "What systems are you working on?" Prof. Sadoway told him about the current status of his research and that the literature he was reading didn't support what he found. His supervisor looked at him and said: "Don, I don't read literature. For one, I find it confusing. Number two, it's full of lies."

The conception of this new battery technology led to the creation of the start-up company Ambri, a spin-off from Prof. Sadoway's lab at MIT.

He founded Ambri in 2010 together with David Bradwell and Luis Ortiz with the vision to produce safe and reliable liquid metal batteries for affordable electric storage solutions. The company has been backed by Bill Gates and the French energy company Total S.A. It is based in Cambridge, Massachusetts, and the companies name comes from the heart of cAMBRIdge. One of the biggest challenges was raising money. *"People don't throw money at an idea. Here's the thing. Someone says, 'We really need a radical innovation.' It's not about improving what exists, but really making a difference. I show them the liquid metal battery. They say, 'Wow, that's radical. How big is the risk of failure?' I tell them, 'Yes, this company can fail. If you don't want to take a risk, you have to make incremental improvements. This is not radical. The integral of infinite incremental improvements is not a breakthrough! Radical innovation is bought with risk - you bet on the potential impact if successful."* At the very time I am writing these lines, five months after our conversation, I read about a big announcement: Ambri is receiving a $144 million investment from Reliance Industries. The money will be used to build production facilities in the US and around the world to meet the growing demand for energy storage devices.

Since liquid metal batteries are basically *"made of dirt"*, as Prof. Sadoway likes to say, they are much cheaper than lithium-ion batteries. Talking about costs of batteries, we start discussing incentives and government subsidies for electric vehicles. Prof. Sadoway has a very strong opinion on this. He starts off very calmly, but from word to word he becomes more and more emotional. *"It will not be cheaper because there are incentives, subsidies, government rebates or penalties for CO_2 emissions as penalty to other cars. No - I want it to be affordable by itself, on its own merit*

26

on the marketplace! This is decarbonization by spreadsheet, but this is not real! It is not economically sustainable." He recalls the incentive programs when Tesla began selling their first electric models. "*I was so angry when we gave incentives in the early days when the Tesla car cost $125,000. If a person has this amount of money, why is the government giving subsidies to these people? This is sick! This is crazy - this is policy going wrong!*" I can understand his frustration about this issue and find it all the more inspiring that he is not content to complain about it but is actively working on a solution. And that's what we need. That's why I consider him an innovative thought leader for our electrified future.

Besides battery safety and cost, Prof. Sadoway adds another requirement for batteries that we heard a lot about in the first chapter. It is interesting that he mentions it as something that was added only recently. It confirms Darshan's concerns and wishes about second life batteries. "*Now, we have another demand. Besides cheap and safe we need to understand what happens to them at their end of life? Can we recycle batteries? Can we reuse them?*" Liquid metal batteries have a very long lifetime of around 20 years. They do not suffer from degradation effects as we know them for the lithium-ion battery chemistry. They don't lose capacity over time. "*With liquid metal technology the battery just continues to work. After 20 years, the metals with the positive and negative electrodes as well as the salt can be refined and reused, and the steel can be remelted. This battery is not going to the landfill. There are only few things in the world that you can recycle in such a way. Most of the times you try to get the constituents, but they are going to go into a different use because their quality after the recycling process is lower. If you take certain polymers and collect them and shred them, you use it for something different because the quality of the materials would be different after that process. Metals, you can remelt. Metals can be eternal. Certain glasses you can reuse, but not with polymers or ceramics. If I break this cup, it's gone.*"

I am impressed by Prof. Sadoway's way of thinking, his mindset, and his personality. Several times during our conversation, I tell him that I am sincerely honored that he shares his life story with me. The way he explains things makes them seem so simple. I will never forget him explaining why liquid metal batteries make so much sense. *"If you are looking at the periodic table, what's the cheapest element? Steel. Iron. But it's kind of heavy. What's the second cheapest metal? Aluminum. Okay, well, that's my anode. What's the cheapest non-metal? Sulfur. Okay, that's my positive electrode. What do I use for the electrolyte? It can't be volatile; it can't be flammable. Molten salt. Okay, let's take molten salt."*

"You invent by thinking what's the end product. The end product has to be cheap! At the university the coolest chemistry gets a paper in a fancy journal. But you can't do that with batteries. I don't care if you make beautiful chemistry if it won't scale! We are competing against gasoline and diesel. You have to think about cost from day one."

ELECTRIC CARS
AND THEIR MULTI-USE

Electrification alone is too simple. We need a whole transformation!
NIO and China were the biggest learning experience for me.
The transformation of an entire industry.
Within a few years, E-mobility moved to the forefront.
That was eye-opening.

ANGELIKA BERGER-SODIAN

May 14th, 2021, UK

CHAPTER 03

ELECTRIC CARS AND THEIR MULTI-USE

C an you imagine that at any given moment of the day, there are one billion cars around the world not being used? That's a huge amount of resources just sitting and waiting, taking up space that could be used for something else. Even if we could electrify the entire global transportation system, could there be a more efficient and better way to use our transportation resources?

This is one of the main ideas of Angelika Berger-Sodian and her colleagues with their start-up MOOV Automotive, which is developing the next generation of electric vehicles that move everyone and everything with optimal efficiency and true sustainability. Angelika has been on a mission to help companies around the world to go electric by developing their organizations and leveraging innovative business models. Early on, she observed the drive, passion, and pace of innovation for companies in China that wanted to be leaders in this electrification movement. She spent a long time at NIO in China developing programs such as E-racing, and the use of these technologies in passenger cars that NIO would sell to consumers. She believes electrification is the future, but not enough to be truly sustainable. She looks at the big picture and wants to change the operating model of the entire transportation sector.

For the first time in this book, we focus on batteries and **Electric Vehicles** in the passenger car segment, the commercial vehicle sector, and motorsports. In this chapter, the battery is considered, from an integration perspective, as the most expensive component in an electric vehicle accounting for around 30% of the total cost.

Electric Vehicle
Manufacturing

Angelika Berger-Sodian
CEO Europe MOOV
Electric Cars & their Multi-Use

First Life In-Use
Electric Vehicles

Angelika was born and raised in Austria, in a town called Villach in the beautiful mountain region of Carinthia (Kärnten). I know this area very well because my mother's side of the family is from Carinthia too. I spent every vacation with my grandmothers in Carinthia and Tyrol with the latter being the roots of my father's side of the family.

The interview with Angelika took place virtually and in German. Angelika was in her apartment in the UK, which she calls her home right now. It is very nice to have this interview in my native language and specially to listen to Angelika's German. She has this very pronounced friendly Corinthian accent. Angelika has a special charisma, which I felt even through my laptop camera. She is warm and yet determined and dedicated and knows exactly what she wants to do. I can learn a lot from her.

I first saw Angelika as the keynote speaker at a conference in Austria. I was delighted to see a woman on the main stage- a rare event in the automotive industry. She spoke about her time with the company NIO in China and how the automotive market and business models in China are different from what we are used to in Europe.

NIO Inc., whose name means "Blue Sky Coming" in Chinese, is a Shanghai-based premium smart electric vehicle producer. The company designs and manufactures electric vehicles, but also offers unique and innovative solutions for the entire electric vehicle market. They were one of the first companies to successfully offer battery swap stations to its customers. In battery swapping, the battery of the electric car is not charged from a charging station, but completely exchanged with a fully charged one in a matter of minutes. It is one of the ways the industry is trying to get electric vehicle charging times similar to traditional refueling. Further, in the last year NIO launched a "Battery-as-a-Service" program. Both battery swap and battery-as-a-service are business models at the forefront of the E-transformation.

Angelika joined the company at a very early stage in 2015, a few months after it was founded by William Li. She led the organizational development in Shanghai and soon she became HR (Human Resource) Director in Europe and finally, in 2019, Managing Director of NIO in the UK. "*NIO was my biggest learning experience. Customers and customer experience are top priorities at NIO. It was enlightening to follow this company on its journey to the forefront of E-mobility.*"

Angelika grew up in a very entrepreneurial environment. "*My parents owned a company in computers and office systems, today called a digital business.*" While her father expected her to take over the business as the only daughter, she soon realized that wasn't an option for her. She admired the beauty of Carinthia and Austria, but she didn't see her future there. Even in elementary school, she dreamed of going to school in Italy. Her parents were surprised and didn't really understand why their daughter wanted to leave so badly. Angelika laughs and says, *"A few years later, my parents would have been happy if it had just been Italy. I really wanted to see the whole world!"*

Because her parents owned their own business, Angelika was exposed to the ups and downs of entrepreneurship at an early age. She remembers discussions at the lunch table where her parents would talk about their business strategy. "We have so much profit, we need to invest so we minimize our taxes" - and then, just a few months later, "We made less revenue than we had hoped, but we have to pay Christmas salary." Angelika remembers, *"These discussions sounded strange to me, but I really wanted to understand how this worked. What is the mechanism behind it? I didn't want to take over my parents' company, but I found the business side very exciting. I wanted that for my life, too - with all the pros and cons. That was the motivation for me to study business and economy."*

Have you always been interested in the automotive world?

Her reply is fast and clear. *"No. I used to watch Formula 1 with my dad on the weekends. Both my parents had really nice cars. In our family, we were the classic end users who really appreciated having cars, having fun washing them on Sundays."* While these memories established a first natural engagement with cars in general, what actually brought her into the automotive world from a professional perspective were her studies of International Management at the University of Graz. *"There were only so many international companies around in Styria that offer their candidates to go abroad. I picked a Thesis with Magna Steyr. This industry has been good to me and really became my comfort zone."* She started her Doctoral Thesis with Magna Steyr, back in 2003, which developed further with two-and-a-half years at Magna Steyr in Austria, one-and-a-half years at Magna in

Shanghai and another year-and-a-half at Magna Powertrain heading up people development and training for Europe and Asia.

Magna Steyr AG & Co KG is an automotive manufacturer based in Graz, Austria. They develop and assemble cars for auto manufacturers worldwide. Angelika emphasizes her background with this first company she worked for after graduation: *"Magna was a very good company for me, and I am very grateful for this foundation. As Magna is an international automotive supplier and manufacturer with comprehensive full vehicle expertise, I gained a very good overview and insight into the various disciplines and dimensions of this industry. I also gained my first leadership experience at Magna at an early stage. Since then, Magna has been a thread running through my life. In all my later positions, I kept finding references to Magna and have started several collaborations with them."*

Angelika started her career at Magna with her doctoral thesis about technology and know-how transfer in international projects. How can we develop mechanisms to pass on information in international projects and learn from one project to the next? *"I have learned to look through the lens of team and organizational development."* The organization- how employees are structured into teams and how they work together- is the backbone of every company and can be the driver to long-term success. She describes this as one of the biggest challenges that many major automakers are facing today during this E-transformation. They need to shift from internal combustion engine cars to electric cars, not only from a technological standpoint but also in terms of corporate structure. All this is happening at a rapid pace and requires restructuring of teams and organizations. *"It's all about change and transformation. Most of the bigger organizations are not positioned nor prepared for this fast transformation."*

How disruptive was the financial crisis of 2008?

Angelika continued her career at Magna until she found herself faced with a difficult decision in Shanghai. *"Suddenly there was the crisis of 2008.*

I began to think about how to position myself for my future career. Should I go back to Austria, or should I dare to try and live out the entrepreneurial desire and risk of building my own business?"

My inner voice screams "entrepreneur!". At the time of my conversation with Angelika, I had just decided to start my own business and was four months in. I was at an energy level of 200%, totally excited and enjoying the newfound freedom to do whatever I wanted.

Angelika told me how she started her own company ACCOD Management Consulting Limited in 2009. "*Given the economic environment, it was the right time in my life to add value in an area where I really knew my stuff. I was supporting automotive companies that wanted to do business in or with Chinese partners. Together with my Chinese partner, Leslie, we helped our European clients get the most out of working with Chinese companies.*"

In 2015, Leslie decided to leave our partnership to work for a startup called NIO. "*That was another decisive moment in my life. I had to ask myself which direction I wanted to go. What direction is the whole world taking? At the time, I thought that big European auto makers would go for China, but they just had a totally different view of the world which did not harmonize with what was happening in China. I completely changed my mind when I looked at how startups were doing business in China. They were even more innovative than I had ever imagined.*"

Angelika paused her own consulting and followed her business partner Leslie to "*build NIO from 0 to IPO.*" IPO means Initial Public Offering and describes the point where shares of a company are sold to investors. She makes this sound very natural and easy. "*Working with NIO in China was a great learning experience. NIO develops and manufactures electric vehicles, but they position themselves as a lifestyle company. They want to create a fundamental and global positive customer experience. We had our own racing team, but not necessarily because we wanted to be part of motorsports, but more for brand strategy reasons. Formula E was something completely new at the time, and we wanted to be at the forefront."*

Indeed, NIO's "Team China Racing" was one of the original Formula E race teams. NIO's high performance electric supercar, the NIO Electric Performance EP1 was designed only for racing and was produced in 2016 as NIO's first electric vehicle. Each of its wheels has its own electric motor and it is equipped with a lithium-ion battery pack and an electric range of 265 miles (472km). It accelerates from 0 to 100 km/h (62mph) in 2.7 seconds and has set records for the fastest lap on an electric vehicle at several global racing tracks. Today, NIO has produced three SUV type passenger car models and by April 2021 they had sold more than 100,000 electric vehicles.

How is NIO at the forefront of innovating electrification?

"They have successfully implemented the concept of battery swapping in China." A battery swap station is a substitute for charging an electric vehicle at a dedicated charging station or at home. It looks like a big container where you park your electric car, take out the empty battery and replace it with a charged one. This process takes about five minutes at an NIO swap station, making it comparable to filling up a gas-powered car at the gas station. This concept is now a reality with the two millionth battery exchange in March 2021 and a total of 193 battery swapping stations in China. NIO has succeeded in combating its customer's "range anxiety" and making the switch from internal combustion engines to electric cars more attractive.

They are not the only company that has explored battery swapping. In 2013, Tesla demonstrated being capable of exchanging the battery pack in one minute and 40 seconds, which is faster than filling a tank at the gas station. Interestingly, Tesla did not pursue this concept and instead focused on establishing a worldwide Supercharger network. With Tesla's latest developments, where the battery pack is a structural part or rather "the structure" of the vehicle, battery swapping no longer works. *"I always liked following Tesla. Elon Musk is a cool guy; he is proactive and innovative. I like Tesla, but for me, NIO is even more innovative. I am a big fan of William Li."* In August 2021, NIO has expanded to Norway and built their first battery swap station in Europe.

Besides battery swapping, Angelika mentions another key innovation for business models in the transportation sector area. *"The whole service and maintenance topic brings up completely new aspects: Transportation as a service – Battery as a service."* Battery as a Service is a concept that NIO launched last summer in 2020 together with the largest battery manufacturer in China, CATL. Battery as a Service is a business model that separates the customer of an electric car purchase from the battery. You buy the electric car, but you subscribe to the use of the battery separately. Since the battery is the most expensive component, accounting for around 30% of the net cost of an electric vehicle, this approach contributes significantly to reducing the purchase price of electric cars.

What role does the battery play for you and your business?

"I had the opportunity to look at the battery from different perspectives. For me, it was fascinating to see how the status of the battery changed over time. When I was involved with the NIO race team in China, it was all about the battery's performance. NIO passenger cars used the battery to differentiate themselves from others, especially with the concept of battery swapping. Now, in our MOOV activities, the battery is a component and potential part of an overall solution. The battery is getting more and more important. In general, I believe that electrification alone is too simple. We need a whole transformation."

Today Angelika is CEO Europe of MOOV Automotive Ltd. MOOV is developing the next generation of electric vehicles that move everyone and everything with optimal efficiency and true sustainability. With their technology solution for urban mobility, they aim to address the fact that more than a billion vehicles on the planet today are at a standstill at any given time. At the time of our interview in May 2021, MOOV is less than a year young. It was founded completely virtually during COVID times. *"Our startup was not only defined technologically and set up product-wise during COVID, but also founded. We did not react to COVID but integrated these special circumstances as a basis into our company framework."* She describes how they are building teams at times where everybody is working from home and how they break traditions and make transactions that are not common for a startup. *"We have an uncompromising focus on talent. We are building our team globally as long as they can be integrated into our platform and willing to work in our time zone. We are differentiating. We are geographically diagnostic and crisis resistant."*

"With MOOV we want to address two challenges. First, sustainability. The current industry is not sustainable. Even if we shift to fully electric." This message is very refreshing. Too often in these times, the hype for electrification is that it will solve all our problems, but Angelika and MOOV take it a step further.

"Basically, it's about solutions that work in the long term - not the short term. If we keep treating our planet this way, we won't have a happy ending. What does that mean for me in my everyday life - I want to act in a way that our next generations and grandchildren will have a beautiful and healthy planet. I'm in my mid-40s, I come from this generation and culture where it's all about having the better career and the bigger car. Too often, sustainability is just lip service. The younger generation now has a different sense of urgency and intrinsic motivation. I think, overall, we can afford to focus on sustainability now. We have very long planning cycles at MOOV."

The second challenge Angelika wants to address with MOOV is multi-use or multi-modality. *"Even shared autonomous vehicles are not enough to be truly sustainable. We are working on a completely new vehicle concept. Our first product will be an electric multimodal van that can be converted for different applications in seconds. With this approach, we will address the challenge that there are too many vehicles on the road."*

I want to learn more but at the time of our interview, Angelika couldn't give me any more insight because MOOV was in the middle of negotiating important strategic business relationships.

She concludes, *"When I was a kid, I wanted to be a florist. Something very different - very creative. I always enjoyed nature and I was always very interested in tourism and the hospitality industry. Now that I've spent my whole professional life so far in the automotive and E-mobility sector and have witnessed this huge transformation, I'm sure there are other industries that are stuck in their traditional thinking and old patterns. Maybe I can contribute to other industries in the future - for example, at the interface between mobility and hospitality."*

THE THIRD WAVE OF ELECTRIFICATION

Since 2000, there have been three waves of electrification.
I am kind of curious to see where this one takes us.

PAUL BEACH

May 7th, 2021, USA

CHAPTER 04
THE THIRD WAVE OF ELECTRIFICATION

Many of you reading this book probably already have experience with electrified transportation. However, some of you may be surprised to learn that there have already been several waves of enthusiasm for electrical power. In previous chapters, decades ago Ford produced an electric vehicle and so did General Motors with its EV1 program. Perhaps at the time these vehicles and these programs were implemented, the population was not ready for the electrification of the car, nor were batteries.

The mindset of typical European and American families was the freedom to pack the family into their SUV and drive anywhere they wanted at any time. They would drive long distances and only stop for 10 or 15 minutes to refuel and then continue their journey. When Ford and GM's first electric vehicles came out, battery technology didn't have the large capacity needed to go many miles between charges, nor did it have the technology to allow fast charging in less than 20 or 30 minutes for a full charge. The current wave of electrification has already addressed some of these challenges and perhaps this is the critical factor for success.

Paul Beach has been heavily involved in prior waves of electrification and has been passionate about batteries from the start. He is very optimistic about this third electric wave but has been burned before. Paul runs a company called Octillion Power Systems, which is probably not well known to the public but is one of the largest manufacturers of battery packs in the world. At a time when governments were funding high-flying battery start-ups that weren't succeeding, Paul's companies were, and are still active today. Paul's chapter in the battery biography is about **Battery Packs** and the **Battery Cells** residing inside them.

Battery Manufacturing
Life: 100%

Paul Beach
President Octillion
Third Wave of Electrification

Today, in 2021, we seem to be in a major paradigm shift, where batteries and electric vehicles are on the rise. Many of the major car manufacturers in Europe, the US and China have declared their withdrawal from internal combustion engine vehicles. So, while a lot of people are all very enthusiastic about this latest electrification trend, I am particularly interested to talk with someone who has been working and actively driving this industry for the past thirty years. Are we in the middle of a big electrification and battery boom? Did this happen before? Will electric vehicles take over the world?

Paul points out that there have already been two massive electrification waves since he got into the battery business, and we seem to be in the third one. *"I would really like to see this one take off. I observed the first two fizzle out in 2001 and 2010. Let's see where this one takes us."*

Paul Beach grew up in Maine, USA. *"We moved a lot when I was a kid because my father was in surgical training. So, I lived in six places before I was six. We bounced around New York, LA and then eventually to Bangor, Maine, a small town of 35,000 people, on the Penobscot River. This is where Stephen King is from, by the way. I had a great childhood getting into a lot of trouble running around the town, jumping trains. I have two older sisters who have always been a close part of my life. Career-wise I didn't exactly know what I wanted to be. I vacillated from wanting to be an architect, to doctor to finally attorney. I did, however, know that I wanted to travel and see the world!"*

During high school and college, Paul developed a passion for philosophy. *"I studied Nietzsche and existentialism. Challenging to penetrate but these readings left a lasting impression. I also took a lot of science coursework. I think my curiosity regarding technical subject matters has helped me with my work in batteries."* After high school Paul decided to go to law school. *"I studied law at the University of Maine and then the University of California, Berkeley."*

What brought you to the battery world?

Paul tries to remember how it all started: *"My battery story kind of began in Japan. Before heading off to law school, I booked a trip around the world. My first stop was Japan."* At that time, you could buy a one way ticket around the world with as many stops as you like as long as you go in the same direction. *"So, I bought this ticket for $1500. I had planned twenty stops for this six-month adventure. Japan, Thailand, China, India, all the places I wanted to see. The first stop was Japan. A friend of mine was living there."* With excitement he describes his first time visiting a completely new country as an American. *"It was very exciting, I was in a new country, could not speak the language. I landed at the airport and had to get to this specific location in a very rural part of the country. I spent a night out in the cold at the train station because I missed a connecting train. I eventually made to my destination."*

What was supposed to be a short visit, grew significantly extended. He fell in love with the country, the people, and the culture. He was offered a job in Japan, decided to stay, and learned Japanese. *"I sat down and I studied Japanese every day for six hours by myself."*

After returning to the US for law school, he spent 2.5 years in the US and then headed back to Japan to attend law school in Tokyo for his last semester. He met a Japanese attorney who was his professor and ultimately lead him to the battery world. Japan is not a bad country to start a battery journey from and speaking Japanese makes it even better. With more than 24,000 patents Japan is globally leading the rechargeable battery patent landscape based on an analysis from 2000 and 2019, followed by South Korea with around 10,000 patents, China with 8,000, US with around 5,000 and Germany with 2,000.

His experience in Japan led Paul to start working for Quallion LLC. Back then Quallion was a battery cell manufacturer in the medical, military, and aerospace industries. Paul started working at the company in 2001 as an Assistant General Counsel. By the time he left the company almost twelve years later when it was sold to Enersys, Paul was the President. During that time he visited Japan a lot. With Quallion being a battery cell manufacturer, he was going to the cathode and anode factories, as well as electrolyte facilities to learn about the technology.

For those of you who are not familiar with the inside of a battery cell, let's take for example a AA battery like the one in your remote control. It has a positive side and a negative side and you have to put it in the right orientation for it to work. In engineering terms, one side is the cathode, the other is the anode. In the case of a lithium-ion battery we have an electrolyte filling the gaps between these and allowing lithium ions to flow during charging and discharging. This is a very simplified picture, more on that in a later chapter.

In his travels to Japan, Paul Beach learned that the anode and cathode are the chemical heart of the battery determining its performance, safety, and life. *"It was so interesting to visit these facilities in Japan and transferring these technologies to the US. We built a factory in Los Angeles for these materials. We set up cathode and anode facilities. It was a really interesting experience for over 12 years, growing that company, but the market was narrow. At some point, I really wanted to get back to the green side and the environmental aspects. I wanted to address the electric vehicle market."*

He switched over from battery cell maker to a battery pack maker for electric vehicles and started to work for Octillion Power Systems. In the automotive world there is a big difference between battery cell and pack makers. You can envision a battery cell maker as the scientist creating the magical chemistry in the cell. There is a lot of physics and chemistry involved. The battery pack makers take the cells and make them into big products that are then installed in vehicles.

Octillion is one of the largest manufacturers of battery systems in the world. The company supplies battery systems for applications ranging from passenger cars to commercial vehicles as well as to stationary energy storage systems and two-wheelers in their first life. *"With Quallion I was a cell maker. And currently, I am a battery pack maker. So I guess, I have been able to see the two different markets. The last nine years I have spent with Octillion producing battery packs for electric buses and trucks and passenger vehicles. We started in China, grew the Indian and the US market as well getting into the European market. We're one of the largest pack makers in China right now. We're producing 2,000 packs a day, making us probably one of the biggest pack makers in the world by volume."*

Paul, are we in the middle of an electrification boom? Has this happened before?

"Since I got into the battery business in 2001, there have been three waves of electrification. The first wave was post 9/11. A couple of things happened. There was the EV1 program by General Motors." General Motors' Electric Vehicle 1, EV1, is considered the first mass-produced electric vehicle of the modern automotive era. From 1996 to 1999 these electric vehicles were made available to customers in parts of North America through lease-only programs. The first generation EV1 used lead acid batteries that provided an electric range of 60 miles (97 km). In later generations, the battery was replaced by the originally planned nickel-metal hydride battery technology, which offered a greater range of about 160 miles (257 km).

In the 2000s, GM's electric cars were perceived very positively by their customers. People started thinking seriously about electric cars. *"And then 9/11 happened."* Paul shares his memories and perspective including how he perceived America's role in the oil industry at that time. All these activities had a critical impact on battery and electrification actions for the next decade. *"The US government did something very fundamental at that point. We focused on hydrogen fuel, rather than batteries. And that was the policy for the next eight years. There was not a lot of money going into batteries. So, batteries just kind of died and went nowhere for electrification for 8 years."*

The documentary "Who killed the electric car?" was published in 2006 as film directed by Chris Paine. It examines the history and limited commercialization of battery electric vehicles in the United States during that time. It analyzes the interplay among various stakeholders, from automakers to the oil industry to the US federal government to consumers during this period. In particular, it shows how General Motors discontinued the EV1 program in the 2000s and scrapped most of the vehicles despite public interest. Paul's memories are in line with Prof. Sadoway's, who mentioned both the initiatives by the Argonne National

Lab in the 60s, as well as Ford's first all-electric vehicle in 1993, had been stopped. This was the end of the first wave of electrification.

"*In 2008, President Obama was elected.*" Paul describes the second wave: "*The economy was down. We had a major recession. There was a huge stimulus package put in place to get America back on its feet. The Obama administration went all-in on electrification.*" Large battery manufacturers were receiving huge funding and investment at the time. The news was filled with headlines like "President Obama announces $2.4 billion in grants to accelerate the manufacturing and development of the next generation of the US Batteries and Electric Vehicles." President Obama said, "If we want to reduce our dependence on oil, put Americans back to work and reassert our manufacturing sector as one of the greatest in the world, we must produce the advanced, efficient vehicles of the future." They provided $1.5 billion in grants to US-based manufacturers to produce batteries and expand battery recycling capacity.

Paul recalls several battery cell manufacturers that were funded by the government back then: "*LG from Korea was funded. SAFT from France was promoted. A123 of the United States, which was domestic, was promoted. There were seven or eight contracts awarded for $1.2 billion.*" At that point, Paul was still working for Quallion LLC, the battery company he had joined in 2001. In 2008, Quallion was one of the largest and oldest lithium-ion cell manufacturers in the United States. But they didn't get governmental financing. "*So, all the factories went to Florida, Indiana and Michigan,*" he explains with a slightly disappointed tone. I sense that he was looking forward to batteries and electric vehicles finally taking off during this time, but that didn't happen. Unfortunately, many of those battery manufacturers that were funded from 2008 to 2012 did not do well, and some of them died.

Why did the second wave not take off and what can we learn for 2021?

"In my opinion, the reason development did not take off in 2008 was that the market for electric vehicles just was not ready. The US can be a very demanding consumer market." American society, especially in Los Angeles, where Paul was living at that time, had this huge boom for big cars. *"Many people preferred larger vehicles. You could see a demand for larger SUVs. These are also more profitable."*

With Octillion, Paul is heavily tied to the Chinese and Indian electric vehicle markets and developed a very good understanding about different habits in different parts of the world when it comes to electrification of the transportation sector. *"The Chinese started the transition to electric much earlier than other countries. They travel about 50 miles a day to commute. The driving habits there make the market amenable to adopting electrification. The government was also looking ahead and planning very strategically how to address climate change and move the country to electrification. That was very forward thinking."*

When being asked how we can adapt towards electrification in the US, Paul mentions California as a good start. *"California is a great example. California is ahead of the curve. We have windmills, we have solar, we have all sorts of renewables. But, if you do not have the energy storage coupled to electricity generation, renewables are very sporadic. The sun goes down and wind energy is very dynamic."* He explains how all that is battery driven: *"We need energy storage coupled to these variable generation sources in order to smooth out the system. You can use that power to supplement the grid, but also to stabilize the inconsistent current that's coming off from renewables. Vehicle to grid could be the next step. If every Californian had an electric vehicle connected to the grid, we could go back and forth with the energy, problem solved. But you would need to force every Californian to get an electric car, then you need to install vehicle to grid infrastructure everywhere, in every office and every home. This will cost a lot of money, which nobody wants to pay. It also stumbles on policy agreement and funding."*

We can learn from Paul Beach about how much impact politics and governments, as well as our society and their mindset, have in the automotive industry. I am reminded of the announcements of the Biden administration right now in 2021, where again a huge push towards electrification and its infrastructure is promoted. *"We are in the third wave of electrification right now. In my opinion this wave is being driven in part by Tesla's momentum and enthusiasm. Also, China has put 450,000 electric buses on the road, and battery prices are down to $100 per kilowatt-hour. In the commercial vehicle sector, the total cost of ownership is already lower than for internal combustion engine vehicles."*

Paul mentions Tesla as a company which has successfully contributed as a backbone to make this third wave the one that potentially stays. *"Tesla saw what people wanted and then made it. Early on, Tesla's business model looked questionable. How can you possibly build a car company in this day and age? Lots of companies thought they could start, but many of them struggled and died. All the traditional automakers thought Tesla would be bankrupt. Finally, Tesla persevered and took over the market."*

In Paul's view, Tesla have fought range anxiety, built a car around technology, and changed the overall user experience. *"Tesla is sustainable on its own. The company pivots, changes, bundles. Tesla is looking into solar, charging stations and even an all-electric truck. Regarding the Gigafactory, I believe they got into the cell making business not to improve margins, but because they wanted to control the supply chain. The company has created this ecosystem around an experience. They are thinking much further down the road than other companies. They see an ecosystem problem and they are building in solutions to address the same."* With a sly smile, Paul adds, *"Better not bet against Tesla- you'll lose very quickly."*

Paul's conclusion: *"I think this third wave is sustainable. Hopefully, we will help it become a better world!"*

CHARGING ELECTRIC VEHICLES FROM THE ROAD

We need engineers with glitter nails and high heels.
You need different things, so everybody can find
something to identify with.

KARIN EBBINGHAUS
June 22nd, 2021, Sweden

CHAPTER 05

CHARGING ELECTRIC VEHICLES FROM THE ROAD

I am sure that most of you reading this book either drive an electric vehicle yourself or perhaps know someone else who does. And we know that people usually charge at home, at work, or at malls and restaurants that also have charging stations. They keep plugging in to charge their vehicles. But what if we took it a step further? What if we planned our routes on similar roads every day, and on some of those roads, we could charge our vehicle while we drive?

This chapter focuses on charging electric vehicle batteries in their **First Life.** We are in the **In-Use** phase of our battery biography diagram, in which electric vehicles are driven by their owners and charged through normal charging stations or a system like the one that Karin wants to industrialize.

From a young age, Karin Ebbinghaus wanted to become as powerful as some of her female idols. After getting a law and a business degree and spending time investing in several different companies, she realized if she really wanted to be effective, she had to be in charge. She didn't want to just be the puppeteer behind the scenes. She wanted to take the risks, not be afraid of the status quo, and make a change in this world. She eventually found her way into the electric vehicle charging area, where she connected with her co-founder. They had a synergy in which his technical expertise and her business savvy and exuberant personality were a perfect match, and she became the CEO of the Swedish startup Elonroad. Karin's aim is to give everybody "range happiness" with their electric vehicles and get rid of the popular term "range anxiety" to accelerate electrification.

First Life In-Use
Electric Vehicles

It is 2018. Through her job at an investment firm, Karin starts working with Dan, the technical founder of Elonroad. Her role is looking for investors to support Dan's innovative idea: create electric roads to charge electric vehicles while they drive. She has been pitching this idea to investors for nearly two years and she really wants this idea to succeed. In 2019, she realizes she wants their success so much that she's considering becoming the company's CEO. *"With Elonroad I couldn't resist. I needed to do it. I thought I will regret it forever if I don't do that. I couldn't let it go. It's so disruptively cool!"* Karin tells me enthusiastically, her eyes wide open and shining. Her passion is contagious. "What is so disruptively cool about Elonroad?" I ask. She has piqued my curiosity. *"It's a total paradigm shift. Historically, when you have a gasoline car you will fill it up at the gas station. Then you drive it. You have the energy on board until you burn it. With Elonroad, we build a system where you have energy at your fingertips. You have access to energy on the go. You don't need electric vehicles with huge batteries, or gas tanks. You will have infinite range."*

Elonroad is a Swedish startup founded in 2014 by Dan Zethraeus. His vision was to build a system of electric roads that would provide the ability to charge electric vehicles while driving. It consists of a conductive rail that is laid on existing roads or built into the road. When driving on these roads, a conductive pickup under the vehicle connects to the electric rail and supplies electricity to the car. This allows the car to be charged while driving. Elonroad stands for electricity which is "El" in Swedish, plus "on", plus "road". *"It is also a flirt with Elon Musk."*

"The concept of charging while driving is not new. Think about railways and trams. They use an overhead electrical system to charge them. But having normal roads to charge all kinds of vehicles, this is new." Elonroad was selected by the Swedish Transport Agency for a pilot program, in which this electrical road system would be tested for three years. In 2019, construction began on "Evolution Road", a one-kilometer electric pilot road in Lund, a southern Swedish province in Skåne. Solaris, a Swedish electric bus manufacturer, is providing an electric bus that will be the first vehicle used in the pilot project.

Lund has a population of 90,000 and currently has ten bus lines. A typical traditional approach for electrifying the bus fleet would be to charge them at their end stations. These ten bus lines would require twenty end station chargers. Alternatively, they investigated an electrical road system. Only ten per cent of the total route length needs to be covered with the electrical road system to supply the buses with charge while driving because some of them partly share the same routes.

With four different electrical road test sites on public roads, Sweden is pioneering the electrical road systems. *"We do have competitors. We are not completely crazy on our own. Of all the companies that are doing electrical roads right now, we are the smallest. We are a team of twelve right now."* She points to Siemens, which uses overhead pantograph charging technology; Evias, another Swedish startup; and an Israeli company called Electreon, which uses a wireless system. *"After this small pilot project, we want to win the next bigger pilot project for over 30 kilometers. One of the reasons I was intrigued by Elonroad is that it has the charging capacity but also a digital aspect. When a vehicle drives over the rails, we are sending an encrypted radio signal to unlock the power distribution within one meter at the time. We only power exactly under the vehicle. It does not matter if you drive 130 kilometers per hour or stand still."*

Karin's entrepreneurial spirit can be traced back to her childhood and the role models she admired. She grew up in a small city in the southern part of Sweden as an only child. With both her parents being academics, it was a natural decision for her to pursue higher studies. *"Although I did have a small rebellion against my father. My father was a medical doctor, but I chose language and communication which he thought was horrible because I should be doing something science based,"* Karin says with a smile on her face. *"Well, finally I went to law school. I didn't have a particular goal to be a lawyer even though I liked watching Ally McBeal on TV. I also do remember watching the movie "Working Girl" with Melanie Griffith and Harrison Ford when I was younger. In this movie she is doing successful business in the city. I thought, I want to sit in a fancy office like that in a big city. With power suits and a briefcase. That was part of my vision. Part of my mood board."*

This reminds me of myself when I was a little girl and wanted to sit in a "boss chair" one day. I remember picturing one of those typical black leather office chairs. This has been on my personal mood board ever since. Today, at the age of 32, I have started my own business. I may not be sitting in a big fancy leather chair in a high up office, but I feel connected to that vision.

Karin began to put her vision into practice right after graduation. In 1999, she started working for the British law firm Linklaters. *"I went to London, got my business suit and did what I dreamed about."*

In 2005, Karin realized that she wanted to have a family and moved back to the southern part of Sweden. Today she has three kids with her husband and lives in Lund. She pursued a very successful career as a lawyer and after earning her MBA degree at the Stockholm School of Economics in Sweden she worked as an investment manager. *"I always worked with private equity. I truly like doing business. I went into investment, and I got a job at a venture capital fund focusing on investments into startups reducing CO_2 in Sweden. I felt this was my dream job, meeting all these talented entrepreneurs who focused on climate change. It was so inspiring."* One of the startups that came searching for funding at the investment firm she worked for was Elonroad. Karin was really intrigued and wanted to help them. But she also realized that they were not investor ready. They were too small, too technical, and not ready for business. *"I introduced lots of people to the founder, but nothing clicked. So, I decided to join the team."*

When Karin joined the Elonroad group, she had a clear vision. *"If I join the team, I want to be the CEO. I wanna be in the limelight. Quite often, especially as a woman, you do all the hard work. You prepare everything, you do everything, but then there is a man stealing the limelight because he is ahead of you. Men take all the credit. I wanted to change this."* Dan welcomed this mindset. *"He said, 'Yeah, go ahead, I like to invent things, and you can be the co-founder."* They found the perfect synergy based on their natural characteristics. *"I'm more of an execution person than an innovation person. When I met Dan, I realized he was the innovation guy, and I was carrying out his ideas. I'm really good at getting things done. That's my core competency, so I should focus on that. In our professional lives, too often we tend to dwell on our weaknesses. But instead, we should work on what we're good at. I am aware that I am not good at certain things, so I just let them be done by somebody else who likes that."*

Did you always want to start your own business?

"Elonroad is the first company I co-founded. In 2000 when I started working with all the startups, I wanted to try it myself, but I didn't have the right idea. I always thought my personality would be better in a startup than in law. But at that time, I was afraid to lose my traditional career, I had these secure jobs as a lawyer and as an investor. Elonroad is the first time in a startup world where you really don't know where to go and what will happen in the future. I have been on the board for several startups but it's not the same as being the entrepreneur yourself."

Looking through Karin's LinkedIn business profile, she lists nine positions as either a board member or chair(wo)man of the board for a variety of different companies covering many different areas. *"I thought I could be a killer board member. Everybody wants to have a lawyer on the board,"* Karin says and laughs. *"I determined quite early in my career that I wanted to be on a board. There are not many females on boards."*

As a board member of a company, you are advising the management to make good decisions, take next steps, and choose directions based on your experience. *"It's very rewarding because you can bring different aspects and best practices with you and apply them to a new company. It's expanding my horizon."* She describes her experience in a typical board member meeting. *"I am quiet until I feel secure in the group. I will listen and observe until I feel comfortable to say something that adds value to the discussion. Too often, as a woman, instead of just confirming others or repeating others like most men do in these conversations, you don't want to take others' time unless your words are really valuable. As a lawyer, I learned it is better to say something rather than be quiet and find the perfect thing to say. You have to act confident."* She is referring back to the movie with Melanie Griffith. *"I think I was inspired by this movie. For women to have power, they need to be where the money is. When I grew up there were not many female lawyers doing business. But then, I realized they don't have the power. They are just the means or the tool, not really the ones who decide what deals are made. That's really where the power is, so I moved to the investor side. As an investor, you are sort of the back seat driver. You tell others what to do, but you don't really do it yourself. It's like a teenager's parent. You have to nag, and you have to follow up. Today, I realize, the greatest challenge is being the entrepreneur yourself and creating the value. I am really driven to be a role model for female entrepreneurs and others to show that it's possible."*

What does the battery mean for your business?

"We need batteries in the vehicles to charge. That's the whole part. You can use the energy from the road to only drive, but of course the goal is to charge the vehicles up while they are in touch with our roads. For the 600 Volts from the rail, we need a converter to get to the right voltage for the battery. You will use simultaneous power to drive but also to charge the battery."

She emphasizes how Elonroad as a company that offers charging solutions needs to be integrated into the whole ecosystem, as such, needs the right exchange with other companies in the battery biography. *"We are a charging provider, but we need information from the automakers. We need more insights from battery and car manufacturers to be able to adopt and prepare our equipment so it can be easily installed in every future system. Historically we were more focused on power electronics on the roadside, but we also need to be engaged on the vehicles side. If there is a new DC/DC converter that is better, we need to know about that. Our approach today is more of a retrofit, but in the future, we would like the vehicle to be prepared and equipped with our pickup and on-board chargers, so they are ready to drive on an electrical road."*

As a charging system provider, Elonroad is closely tied to utilities and power generation. Karin emphasizes the importance of using electricity from green sources such as solar, wind and hydroelectric power. Sweden has a good infrastructure and energy landscape to make this possible. Karin and Elonroad can be part of the overall energy system. As such, they could help optimize the flow of energy between electric vehicles and utilities.

Not only can electric roads be used to charge electric vehicle batteries, but excess energy from the batteries could also be fed back into the grid. *"We want to communicate with the batteries and check their status: What is your current state of charge? How much more energy do you need right now to get to your next destination? Are you capable of providing energy if there is a shortage in the grid? If we know the vehicle type and the battery state and know the grid solution, we can intelligently distribute the energy to all the vehicles. We can be part of the total energy system."*

One of the most important benefits for electrical road systems and charging electric vehicles while driving is that you can significantly reduce the size of the battery, and thereby the weight of the vehicle. The 85-kilowatt-hour battery in a Tesla S weighs around 1,200 lbs (544kg) which is 26% of the overall vehicle weight. With electrical roads and energy on your fingertip, the capacity and weight of batteries could be significantly smaller. *"With 6000 kilometers electrical roads in Sweden you will not need a bigger battery than 20-40 kilowatt-hours and you could go everywhere. It could be truly disruptive. It is a vision, and we are doing baby steps. But we have the ambition to be almost everywhere so we can drive with small batteries and talk about range HAPPINESS."*

When being asked what she thinks about battery swapping, Karin has a clear opinion. *"Battery swapping is not my favorite because you need more batteries for swapping solutions. Our view is to minimize the size and demand for batteries. Battery swapping is sort of against that."*

What is a challenge for you?

"People are afraid to make the wrong technology choice. You have a whole menu of options: Battery, hydrogen, biogas. There are so many ways you can go, and you have advocates for different solutions. In Sweden, there is basically no one disagreeing that we have a climate crisis. It's a political will and a financial will. IKEA plans to have fossil free transportation in 2025. This means, that every process connected to IKEA needs to be fossil free. That's a

commitment to their consumers. And a big pressure to fulfill that. The big car manufacturers did not see that change coming. It came much faster than they expected - and wanted. We are standing in front of a tsunami for electrification. A tsunami first goes back, sprinkles a little bit on the surface, but then it will be a flood of electrification. It could not be a more exciting time being in transportation and electrification, but we need to take action. A lot of the people are afraid to bet on the wrong horse, so they do nothing. They wait, instead of trying, learning, failing. The greatest challenge for me is the status quo."*

Another challenge is finding the right people to support Elonroad in its progress over the long term. *"It's very hard to hire people right now. Skipping from one job to the next is very common."* While this problem is mentioned by almost all the interviewees in this book, Karin has a refreshing take on this shared concern: *"I believe it is not necessary for everyone to stay forever. After two years you are most valuable to the company because you have learned a lot, but hopefully the company would get somebody from another company to bring their insights into effect. This is a pool of talent to be exchanged between companies. It's a good thing that people change jobs – sometimes they must move forward. You lose talent but if you are a good company that treats people well, you attract new talent. What goes around comes around."*

Karin is a role model to me, and I am very thankful that I got the chance to talk with her. I am at the beginning of my career and my entrepreneurship. Her interview helped me reflect about how I want to do business. She opened my mind. She strengthened my confidence. I like interacting with confident and powerful women. It is inspiring. I hope the automotive industry and other "gender biased industries" will embrace diversity and not underestimate the power of role models. We all are inspired by people we can identify with.

Karin couldn't find better words: *"We need to have more women. Sometimes when you enter a room you want to find people that you can identify with. Imagine a group of lawyers. They all look the same. We need engineers who have glitter nails and high heels. You need different qualities, so everybody can find something to identify with!"*

ELECTRICITY GENERATION

I started working for TAE and it changed my life.

MIKHAIL SLEPCHENKOV
April 15th, 2021, USA

CHAPTER 06

ELECTRICITY GENERATION

We all use electricity almost every day of our lives. Whether it is in your home, office, or maybe you are even using electricity right now to read this book on your Kindle. Electricity is all around us. But how many of you have ever thought about where that electricity actually comes from? Does it come from a green energy source like solar or wind power, or do we use a traditional energy source like coal, oil, or gas?

Often opponents of electric vehicles cite power generation as a reason why electric vehicles don't make sense. That is partially true. Only when we solve the problem of electricity generation can we make battery-powered solutions the green technology they can truly be.

Mikhail Slepchenkov, who was born and raised in Russia, is not only taking on the challenge of power generation but is turning it into an opportunity. His journey has taken him to TAE Technologics in California where he explores how nuclear fusion can be used to generate electricity in a clean, sustainable way that, when combined with renewable energy, could transform our power grid into one without the pollution of conventional energy sources. By linking electricity generation and energy storage in batteries for electric vehicles, Misha and TAE Technologies are leveraging a synergy to pave the way for this E-transformation.

In terms of battery biography, Misha is active in almost all sectors. Green **Electricity Generation** can be seen in the diagram as the center of the battery biography, supporting every single step from battery manufacturing to charging and recycling.

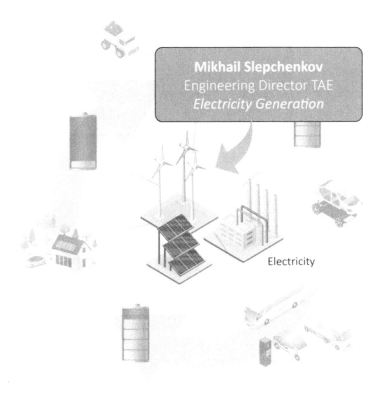

Mikhail Slepchenkov
Engineering Director TAE
Electricity Generation

Electricity

"I was born in Russia in 1977." Misha rolls his "R" the way you expect from someone who grew up with Russian as his mother tongue. His full name is Mikhail Slepchenkov. I interviewed him through a laptop screen, just like all the other Zoom meetings during COVID time, while sitting in my apartment in Milwaukee. Misha seems to be floating in space. He has one of those fancy background animations which, in his case, looks like atoms connected to molecules moving through a galaxy. *"I went to a regular school and a regular university in Russia. I have one younger brother. In high school, I decided to become an electrical engineer. During my studies, I quickly fell in love with my specialty: power electronics."* Being asked what he wanted to be when he was a kid, he remembers: *"People always said. If you want to make money, become a lawyer. If you want to be free, become a musician. So, I decided to become an engineer."*

After his engineering degree, he began his doctoral studies in the field of power electronics. It takes him some time to remember the title of his doctoral thesis: "*The reactive and distortion power compensation in the power systems with nonlinear loads.*" I nod in agreement, trying to show that I understand what he is talking about, but then I start laughing. First, because I couldn't remember the title of my dissertation either, but when it finally came to me, it sounded as pieced together and inaccessible as his. We conclude that one purpose in writing a doctoral thesis must be to impress or confuse one's counterpart with a collection of words that sound highly complex and theoretical - if you can remember them.

With his doctorate in his pocket, he initially devoted himself to a purely academic career. He stayed at the university, continued his research, and enjoyed teaching. "*I was a lecturer, and I got a position as an assistant professor at my university. I developed the course for power electronics and supervised PhD students. It was so exciting to see that I could generate something interesting for these students and they would use this knowledge in the future to create something new. I was happy with what I was doing but one day I realized that I was only doing theory. Also, the funding situation was bad in Russia. I was thinking: If I continue doing simulation maybe I will never see anything that is working in real life. I wanted a change.*" He had two choices: To wait in Russia and hope things would get better, or to try something new elsewhere.

He decided for the latter and began applying to several European universities and research institutes to start a new adventure in a technology field he thought was promising. "*I applied to many positions in Europe. Some interviewed me, but they didn't hire me. I applied for the technical university ETH in Zurich. They received my paperwork but told me I was not qualified enough.*" It is so refreshing to hear someone talk about rejections, to talk about what didn't work, in such a natural and carefree way. "*At some point I thought: Okay, I'll try the US. That's a bit far away, but okay. I typed two words into Google search: Power Electronics + Postdoc +*

California." This was the beginning of Misha's American adventure. A big step from a personal point of view, and the beginning of an extraordinary career.

Today, Misha is Director of Engineering at TAE Technologies. On their website it says in big and wide letters: "Visionary applied science". TAE was founded in 1998 to develop the ultimate clean energy solution: a commercial fusion power source that is compact, cost effective, capable of sustaining the planet for centuries, and safe in every way. You can think of it like this: nuclear fusion occurs when two or more atoms melt together to form another bigger atom. During this process a huge amount of energy is released which we can be turned into electricity. It is the main process that powers stars, including our sun – two little hydrogen atoms fuse into helium. Since 1940, researchers have been exploring various ways to harness this vast energy source for electrical needs. *"One day I saw a video where different nuclear fusion reactors were compared with airplanes. In the beginning, planes had moving wings. People realized that we needed to go up, but we didn't know how and what the final way to do it was. For fusion we know we will be there, but we don't know how the reactor will look. But one of the solutions will be adopted by industry. At TAE, we believe we are on the right path."*

Today TAE has expanded their portfolio from energy creation through fusion to energy storage and E-mobility. TAE is developing electric car platforms, charging and energy storage systems. It is a unique synergy in the industry: products that store and deliver energy on demand are fused with energy generation. *"If you look at the current situation in the energy system, you understand that even with electric vehicles, we're not going to solve the problem. You still need energy to produce and charge batteries. To me, it is very clear. The amount of electricity needed to manufacture batteries and charge electric vehicles is greater than what we need for combustion engine vehicles. So, we need to build a green system and solve the energy problem. And we have to do that at the same time: Produce vehicles and think about where to get the energy from. We have a perfect synergy here at TAE. We need to find a new source of energy because renewables will not be able to provide all the energy we need. Renewables will always be there, but we need nuclear fission, and we need fusion. In the beginning we will coexist with other types of electricity, but sooner or later we will need to change from fission to fusion. In my opinion this is the only way to generate the amount of electricity our planet will require in the future in a clean and safe way.*"

Thinking in terms of our battery biography, at TAE, Misha is covering many areas. He is supplying electricity to all stages along the battery value chain, and he is considered as a battery integrator that makes a platform out of batteries. As such, he needs to consider what happens to his batteries when they are used by clients in the end. And what happens to the batteries once they are not used in TAEs platform vehicles any longer.

What is the value of a used battery?

"*That's one of my favorite topics! The value is high! We need to squeeze the maximum out of these batteries before they go to recycling. I really mean maximum. This is why, at TAE, we are developing this modular system technology that allows monitoring the state of health of each individual battery module.*" He starts comparing batteries to us humans, mentioning his parents when they get older: "*You need to take care of them. You need to be gentle and take an eye on them. You call them more often and ask them how they are doing. This is the same with batteries. If you care about them, they live longer. You provide a doctor's service to these batteries.*" How does a doctor's service for batteries look? "*We need to have a medical card for the battery. We need to know what happened to them, their bios, their history. We need to monitor their state of health on each individual module. There are different approaches. We, at TAE, build modular converters sitting on one or two batteries and monitor and control the power flow to and from these specific modules.*"

Misha's thoughts will probably remind you of our first chapter, where Darshan was emphasizing the importance of tracking electric vehicle batteries in their first life application to be able to reuse them in their second life. Darshan mentioned this as a prerequisite to understanding the state of health of a battery. Misha's reply to a battery's potential second life is a resounding: *"Absolutely yes. We must use these batteries in energy storage systems after they are done in electric vehicles. At the end of their life in an electric vehicle these batteries should be taken together with their passport and current data, and this should be transferred to the company that reuses them. The residual capacity is very important but also other parameters like internal resistance and impedance. We want our battery modules to be reused and repurposed in second life applications without any further refurbishment."*

Do we need a better battery technology or are we ready for a global electric vehicle rollout?

"People still think with old stereotypes. You tell them the car will be running for 200 miles, but they compare that to a gas tank. But with an electric car you charge overnight, and your 'tank' is full every morning. Is it difficult to plug in the vehicle for overnight charge? It takes 30s to plug it in. People need to take a little more care how and when to charge the car, but you can do it!"

What about long-distance driving? *"Unfortunately, sometimes we need to travel long distance and we really need this big battery capacity to get to another city. Sometimes I need to go to San Francisco. During this long trip I usually take two stops. Each stop takes me 15-20 minutes. You stop because you need to go to the bathroom or buy ice cream for the kids. You wait for them, there might be a line at the restroom. You have a coffee and boom - 20 minutes are over. In 20 minutes, you can charge a Tesla at a fast-charging station from almost empty to almost full."*

He concludes: *"We are already quite good with the batteries we have right now, but in my opinion we need to improve the vehicle efficiency.*

Increasing efficiency is important to save the planet. Efficiency means saving energy. Improving efficiency on the vehicle level means smaller batteries which means lower weight and less cost. I believe we need to reduce the cost. I am not buying an electric car because it is more expensive that I can afford. I like the Ford Mustang Mach-E. It's a cool car but more expensive than I can pay. The Audi e-Tron, the new one with three motors. It's amazing technology but too expensive." He has a glow in his eyes when he is talking about the technology in these cars.

What's the biggest challenge for you and your business?

"*Finding the right people. There is a negative unemployment rate for people with expertise in electric cars, batteries and power electronics.*" Misha joined TAE in 2010 when there were 50 people in the company. Every Friday they had lunch together and everybody knew each other. Today, in 2021 they have grown to 250 employees, and they want to grow further. "*Besides finding good people, another challenge in today's day and age, is keeping them. You build them up and then they leave.*" Misha spends a few heartfelt minutes explaining the challenges with the workforce today. He puts so much energy and heart into each of his employees and teams. And after spending many extra hours with them in the lab sometimes they leave for their next adventure.

He recalls moments where they are disassembling batteries in the lab and Misha, as the Director of Engineering, would insist to be there in person. It makes him think back to the times he joined TAE: "*When I joined TAE in the beginning I was thinking, hey, I have a PhD, I know what I am doing. But then I realized that if I think like that, I will never be successful. I started to work with the team and learned from them. Normally, guys with a PhD or Postdoc prefer not to work in the lab, they don't know how to use the tools. But I went there and asked all the technicians how to work with the machines in our workshop. That was fantastic. Today, when we do the reviews with the mechanical and electrical design teams, I know all the* details. I know how it is done because I did it myself. There are times when the team is working on things not necessarily directly related to the main subject of projects. Sometimes my team asks me, 'Misha, why are we doing that, it's not the main part of the project?' I am trying to teach them that we need to be curious about everything. We only have one life and one opportunity to grow professionally. Everything you learn, if you don't use it now, you use it later. The skills that you get now are invested in you. I hope, in the future they will say, 'Thank you Misha - now I know'."

Would you consider yourself having a good "Work-Life Balance"?

"I didn't use to have one, but it came recently. I was taking some Dale Carnegie classes. They teach you how to communicate, how to be a leader, be more open to the world and how to find this balance. I am trying to implement this right now. My boss was encouraging me to take my vacation, but I always had this uncomfortable feeling. I had so much to do, and I thought I needed to work hard all the time. Today I am getting better at this. Now I take my time to reset. I call it recharging my biobatteries because I will be coming back with new energy, and I will do better. I don't say 'I am sorry'. I just take my time off. And I am finding more time with my family. I have two daughters."

Misha, what motivates you? What drives you?

"When I joined TAE, I was so proud to be part of this team where they all have the vision to change the world by working on the edge of the technology. I am motivated by finding a solution to the energy problem. I am 100% sure that the things I am working on are awesome. I always think about if we are taking the right direction and path for our team and our company. I have a goal to grow every day and gain new knowledge. I wanna grow. It feels good! Every day, something new. Sometimes at 11pm I need to force myself to go to bed because I can't stop reading. This work that we are doing gives me that energy and food to learn something new every day. TAE has changed my life."

71

BATTERY RECYCLING

When I set my mind to something, I stick to it and
see it through - by hook or by crook. Sometimes I go to extremes.
I see problems as personal challenges and take them on.

ASTRID ARNBERGER

August 10th, 2021, Austria

CHAPTER 07
BATTERY RECYCLING

Picture this. You try to change the channel of your TV with the remote control, but it doesn't work. Yep, the batteries are dead. You take the old batteries out and replace them and probably throw the dead batteries into the garbage. Of course, if you are environmentally concise you will save them for the battery box you find at work or the local grocery or hardware store. But even then, after you put the dead batteries into the box, what happens then? Have you ever thought about that?

This is one of the biggest challenges that is also facing the electric vehicle market. What happens to all of these electric vehicle batteries after they are dead. We now know, of course, that many of them could be reused or repurposed in other applications. But what if the battery pack is not designed to be disassembled easily to reuse those batteries and, at some point, it will need to be recycled.

Astrid Arnberger has always loved taking on difficult technical challenges. This passion was one of her driving forces during her doctoral studies, which led her to be one of the first in Europe to find a way to recycle electric vehicle batteries. During her PhD, she developed a battery recycling method that was very successful on the lab scale. Of course, doing it in the lab is one thing, but scaling it up to industrial levels is another. Astrid eventually joined the Austrian waste disposal and recycling company Saubermacher, where she is currently the head of R&D for recycling technologies. Most importantly, they have managed to scale up her lab processes for recycling batteries to an industrial scale with 10,000 tons of battery material every year.

Let's investigate **Battery Recycling**, as a very important final step in the battery biography. It can also be seen as the first step for a new battery made from recycled battery material. This is where the battery biography reincarnates.

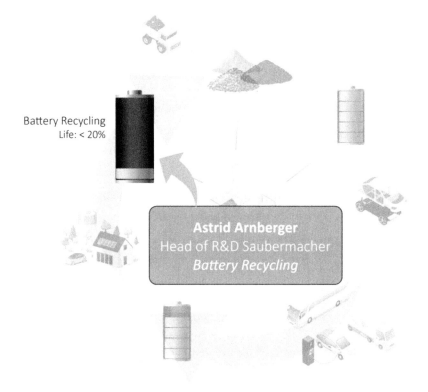

Astrid Arnberger is Head of Research and Development at Saubermacher in Austria. Saubermacher Dienstleistungs AG is a waste disposal and recycling company founded in 1979. Their vision is zero waste. Saubermacher is a German word that literally means "Clean maker" or "Cleaners Group". Annually, Saubermacher processes about 3.5 million tons of waste and serves 4200 customers in 8 countries. The company's headquarters are located in the suburbs of my hometown of Graz, Austria. I know Saubermacher mainly from waste collection and disposal in Graz. Right now, I can imagine their red garbage trucks in my mind. In my discussion with Astrid, I quickly learned that Saubermacher has a very strong focus on research and development and works extensively with universities and partners to continuously develop breakthrough technologies and processes.

When Astrid started her doctoral studies at the Montanuniversity in Leoben, Austria, they picked Saubermacher as an industrial partner. From 2010 to 2016, she developed and pioneered a recycling process specifically for electric vehicle batteries. What she defined and developed on an academic 100kg scale, was finally brought to reality in a large-scale plant in Germany in 2018. She says, *"I had the opportunity to implement my process, which I had tested on a small scale as part of my dissertation, on a ton scale. The plant is approved for 10,000 tons of battery material. It is an incredible feeling when you can put your dissertation into practice and go from 100 kg on paper to a real, industrialized giant plant. And we did it, with all the technical teething troubles that came with it. We encountered a lot of new problems due to the fact that we had to upscale the process."*

Were you aware at the time that you were working on such an innovative idea and basically pioneering battery recycling?

"No, I wasn't really aware of that at the time. I just wanted to find a solution to this problem. And the more we looked into it, the more questions came up. It started with how to safely transport used electric vehicle batteries and how to store them. Then, how do we get the energy out of the batteries before we disassemble and recycle them? We connected a light bulb to the battery to get the energy out. When the light went out, I knew the battery was dead. We had different colored lights; our container looked like something out of a Christmas movie. It got pretty hot in there." She laughs and reflects, *"It was finding answers to these questions that really motivated me. By the completion of my PhD, we had grown into a big team with three other PhD students, and I had learned so much."*

Astrid grew up in Vienna, Austria's capital, with a sister who is four years younger. *"I grew up in a healthy middle-class family, very grounded, nothing special, very down-to-earth. My parents always made sure that my sister and I were doing well - now and in the future. They wanted a good education for us."* She doesn't remember what she wanted to be as a child. *"I think at first I just wanted to try to be like my parents. My mother was an accountant."*

Later, she realized she was more interested in the technical side. *"During my first four years in school, I realized I was completely untalented in languages. Then when I took Spanish as a second foreign language, it was an absolute disaster. But mathematics I loved, and I was really good at it."* Astrid decided to switch to a more technically oriented education and went to HTL, an Austrian technical high school. *"I chose industrial engineering with a focus on environmental technology. I saw a future in that subject."* Her intention or mentality was not necessarily to "save the planet", but she simply thought that the number of issues and challenges for environmental topics will only increase in the future. *"My main focus even then was recycling and waste management."* After high school, she looked for options to intensify her interests in higher studies. *"There were not many options back then. I wanted a balance between technology and economy, not too biological and not too much process engineering."* She started her studies in "Industrial Environmental Protection" at the Montanuniversity in Leoben, not far away from Graz. She focused on disposal technology and waste management.

Back then, the curriculum did not include battery recycling. Astrid remembers topics like the acidification of the soil as well as a big moment during her master's studies, in 2004, when Austria banned the landfill for untreated garbage. It was no longer allowed to pile residual waste. By law, garbage needed to be recycled. *"Waste takes the path of least resistance. If there is a cheaper solution, waste will go there. Recycling competes with landfills. If dumping waste is allowed, it happens. Recycling is often more expensive. As long as there is no legislation, it will be done."* Looking at the situation here in the US and other parts of the world, I need to agree with Astrid. When I came to the Midwest, I was pleasantly surprised to see some hilly areas on this otherwise flat and plain area in Wisconsin, only to realize that these were real garbage piles. A "trash mountain" that people can ski down in the winter.

After finishing her bachelor's and master's studies in minimum time, Astrid's professor convinced her to start her doctoral studies in the field of battery recycling. *"I thought, that could actually be exciting. E-mobility was slowly developing in the European areas at that time. It was coming to us. To my knowledge, nobody in Austria investigated electric vehicle battery recycling and also for Europe battery recycling was kind of rare. There were things happening in China, but their legislations and requirements for the process were totally different. Also, many of the consumer electronics batteries were increasingly using lithium-ion technologies so, thinking about the future potential of that, I was all in. Sounds good! Let's do it!"*

"I started pretty much with a white space, a pen and a paper. In 2010, it was not so easy to get batteries from electric vehicles. The first car batteries I looked at were built in Graz. At that time, they were lithium iron phosphate batteries. We didn't know what they looked like or what they were made of. Okay, they have a metal case, but what's inside?" Astrid needed to start with the basics. She identified two potential techniques to recycle car batteries: either purely mechanical, by crushing the battery into small pieces, or a mixture of thermal pre-treatment followed by a mechanical process. *"We decided to go with the second option. We didn't know then - and we still don't know now - how much battery technology would change over time. At that time, the industry was already talking about solid-state batteries, and we weren't sure if a purely mechanical treatment would work for them. Same with lithium metal, we were pretty sure that wouldn't work without thermal pre-treatment."*

As a battery recycler, you need to understand a lot more than just how to process the material. You may be responsible for the transportation of old batteries to your recycling facility, you have to safely store old batteries until they are processed, you have to get rid of the energy that is still in them. Once the battery is fully discharged, you need to disassemble the pack into smaller pieces and then start the recycling process. *"At Saubermacher we have the following generalized process: we get the batteries, we discharge them, we disassemble them into smaller pieces, we thermally pre-treat them and then mechanically shred them. From that we get the so called 'black mass' which is our current end-product. Black mass is then forwarded to other downstream recycling companies."*

Astrid mentions several challenges a battery recycler is facing in today's battery technology circus. It starts with seemingly simple things. Which battery are you? Which chemistry? How old are you? Are you safe to be disassembled? How can I best discharge you?

"Years ago, when we started to look into battery recycling, we needed to flip the battery around three times with a crane to get all the screws out to disassemble it. Battery packs used to be glued together, so it was very hard to open them. We needed thirty different screwdrivers because of the variety of screws used in the pack." This is why Astrid became active and regularly made suggestions to battery manufacturers on how to improve battery design for recyclability. *"We invited battery designers to our facility to show them how we disassemble their packs. They were surprised about the brute force approach and all the challenges we face to disassemble and prepare the batteries for recycling."*

Saubermacher is collaborating with battery and auto makers and is regularly involved in workshops, research programs and projects where battery manufacturers, integrators and automakers meet to improve the overall battery design and manufacturing process to make it easier to recycle. *"In one of these workshops we were discussing why we can't have the* electronic part of the battery completely separated and accessible." This would be easier for Saubermacher because electronics is recycled separately from the rest. Back then the electronics were distributed over the whole battery pack, and it was really hard to get it separated from the actual battery. Astrid was surprised that the reason was actually to prevent the theft of these electronic parts, as they contained a lot of precious metals like gold.

"Working in research projects is really interesting. We were invited to workshops organized by a university to talk about the battery value chain. We had all different stakeholders at the table. Battery cell makers, battery pack integrators, automakers, and recyclers. It was so interesting to see how we all had our own different pain points and how something that was so critical to me was not important at all to somebody else at the table. It was interesting to understand each other's perspectives. I could not imagine what it means to be a battery manufacturer and how important this intellectual property is to them. I think it was very important for everybody to be at the same table at the same time openly discussing their issues."

How do you deal with E-mobility and recycling in your private life?

"Recycling and waste separation have always been a high priority. Since we live in a single-family house, we have room for different trash bags for each type of waste. We collect everything in the basement and then take it to the proper disposal sites. We also collect Nespresso capsules and have started keeping PET bottle caps separate. We compost our organic waste. It's very convenient in Vienna, where recyclable waste disposal is free. You just collect it and dispose of it for free. When I lived in my apartment in Leoben in a single household during my studies, I couldn't be bothered to separate everything. The quantities were not sufficient, and it was very inconvenient."

Lots of people have the concern about how much energy is needed as we shift to electric vehicles. I am sure you have heard of the claim "If every person plugged in their electric car at the same time, the electric grid would collapse". Austria's primary electricity generation is comprised of already more than 80% renewable energy sources with a feasible plan of 100% by 2030. There are calculations showing that Austria would only need an additional 15% of green energy generation to cover every single Austrian driving electric. Sounds like a pretty good situation.

"Driving electric has not been a topic for our family until recently, simply because, electric cars have been very expensive. My requirements for a car are quite straight forward: It should have four wheels to bring me from A to B and it must be safe. I need a good range to commute between Vienna and Graz. 400km on one charge is a prerequisite for me. And yes, I want to drive at maximum speed on the highway and I don't want to sweat in the summer nor freeze in the winter." She laughs. Lots of her colleagues at Saubermacher are now switching over to electric cars, herself included. *"Last year I signed up for an all-electric company car, the Skoda Enyaq. We did not get it yet, because there were supply difficulties as in a lot of industries. I am really excited to try this! Saubermacher has installed lots of charging ports at their facilities and I can charge at home. I am really curious to try it here in Austria first and get comfortable with it, before we do our first big family trip to Croatia in an all-electric car."*

What is your vision for our electrified future?

"The green deal with CO2 neutrality by 2050 through circular economy is really important to me. There will be a huge focus on waste disposal and finally we have realized that we need to utilize our resources in a circle." Our human brain is used to linear processes. We make a product; we use it, and we get rid of it. But what if we could recycle the old product, get the raw materials back and produce a new product from it? We use the materials in a circle. This is what we call a circular economy. Just recently, there have been announcements about batteries in electric vehicles produced from recycled ones. *"It makes no sense to landfill and burn resources if it is not necessary. Of course, it is not always possible to get back 100% of the initially used materials, because there are certain impurities that*

must be fed to a sink. But overall, a circular economy approach makes sense for lots of industries. Plastics and packaging for example. We have huge amounts of plastics. We can use mechanical and chemical recycling to build a circular economy. The same with wood or metal. Circular economy is better for these cases. I want to see that happening for batteries too!"

"We have become a 'throw-away' society." She is mentioning her smartphone as an example. The initial cost is $300. The only reason we won't use smartphones any more after a couple years is because of the battery. "Replacing the battery with a new one is around a third of the price of a new smartphone. That's too much, so you are tempted to buy a new phone." Talking about the value and price of products in general Astrid has a very nice approach: "You have to consider the effort that goes into producing something. Let's do an exercise. Look at your coffee machine. If you were to produce your own coffee machine, what would you need to do? Where does the coffee come from, where do the beans come from? The machine, the filter, the electricity to power the machine. Think about where to get the plastic from for the machine, how is it made?"

"You can buy a coffee machine for $15. Is this the right price point? Is this reflecting the real value? We somehow lost the connection to these efforts and the value of products. If you do thought experiments like that you start to realize what large-scale industrial processes really mean." Astrid used these kinds of thought-provoking experiments when she was teaching courses during her doctoral studies to make students reference back to products. "With my son, we are growing "bio" vegetables in the garden. The whole process costs a fortune compared to the vegetables you can find in the supermarket, but for me it is important to instill these values in my son."

Are we in the middle of an electrification and battery boom?

"I believe there were several battery waves already. There was the lead acid battery wave. Then there were nickel metal hydride batteries, but they were quickly replaced by lithium-ion batteries. In my opinion, E-mobility is here to stay, but I think it will be a mix of battery electric vehicles and fuel cell electric. And we can't forget about all the batteries from devices that will need to be recycled too. I am very confident that we will have enough batteries to recycle in the future and Saubermacher's recycling plant will be fully utilized. Our competition is looking into different recycling procedures than us. I believe that each of these procedures will have their justification."

MANAGING BATTERIES STARTING AT THE ATOM

Already in school I thought about doing my own thing one day.

Maximilian Ceblin

April 29th, 2021, Germany

CHAPTER 08
MANAGING BATTERIES
STARTING AT THE ATOM

By now, we've already covered several chapters inside of the battery biography. We have met companies making battery cells and packs, installing them into electric vehicles as well as reusing and recycling them. I think it's clear that the history of the battery through its entire first life and second life is very relevant. How is the battery actually used? How often is it charged and discharged? What temperatures was it used at? All these things affect the battery's safety and lifetime. The next chapter delves into the topic of controlling the use of the battery during its life in an electric car.

Nerd alert! This one might get a little technical.

Of course, we all know what a battery is. But I bet only a few of you have thought about what happens inside the battery on the atomic and molecular level in order to store and deliver the electricity that is used to power different devices. I was deeply fascinated by this microscopic view of how things work ever since I got my PhD in quantum mechanics. Everything can be broken down into molecules made of different atoms made of many electrons. Having a good understanding of what happens inside of a battery cell on that microscopic level, during charging and discharging, during rest periods, or in times of extreme cold or extreme heat is needed to keep a battery alive and safe.

Maximilian Ceblin has never been one to shy away from a challenge. His determined personality propels himself to become an expert in things that challenge him. Maximilian is a young entrepreneur with the mentality of many young people who want to do something on their own. And, as they say, if you find a career that is fun, exciting, and even helps the world, you will never "work" a day in your life. The word "entrepreneur" implies that you take risks and that you may have doubts. If you don't take those risks and you don't overcome those doubts, you will never accomplish anything. Maximilian followed this philosophy throughout his education and is putting it into practice in his new startup, which focuses on battery management systems for electric vehicles.

Maximilian Ceblin fits into the **In-Use** chapter of the battery biography. He develops a way to monitor the battery in an electric car on the atomic level to make it long living and to keep it safe.

Battery Manufacturing
Life: 100%

Maximilian Ceblin
Co-Founder Zeta Battery Solutions
Managing Batteries Starting at the Atom

First Life In-Use
Electric Vehicles

Maximilian Ceblin was born in Ulm, Germany, in 1989. *"While growing up, I quickly realized that I had very different interests from my friends."* At the age of twelve, while Maximilian's friends were reading

Manga books, he was reading about science. His grandma gave him a subscription to a German science magazine, *Bild der Wissenschaft*. "*I was fascinated by science from an early age. I did a lot of tinkering. I built rockets with parachutes and enjoyed model making.*" At school, he developed even more interest in science and technology. During the summer vacation, he studied the entire chemistry book for the next school year and enjoyed it. "*Natural sciences and chemistry were set for me at an early age. Because of my dyslexia, I was at war with languages…to the dismay of my family,*" he laughs. With a warm tone, he describes a typical family get together: "*In our family we love to discuss. During family gatherings, we discuss in big rounds, either about politics, which always ends with an argument, which is why we then move on to literature and philosophy. Education is highly valued in our family. My grandma used to take me aside and tell me 'Learn something. What you have in your head, no one can take away from you,' she used to say. She was a war refugee. What she said has influenced me greatly and has become my motto in life: Be curious, explore and keep learning.*"

When asked if he always wanted to do his own thing, he answers with a resounding "*Yes!*" and mentions both his grandmother and his aunt and uncle having run their own businesses. "*My grandparents started a curtain factory after World War II. My uncle was a builder. And he had a passion for fast cars that he shared with me growing up. Watching Formula 1 or visiting the Mercedes Museum in Stuttgart were moments that definitely shaped my path. They were building blocks for my early enthusiasm for technology and grew my interest towards the automotive world.*"

Although Maximilian had a clear interest in science, it was not so easy for him to decide what to do after graduation. "*I struggled with myself. I used to be active in youth work as a scout and a youth leader. Up until a couple of years ago, I was involved at the board level in character development and teamwork doing training. That was this big social aspect. I think I got that from my mom, who also works in a social field. But then I also had to join the military after school. It felt a little bit like a conflict with myself, because at*

88

that point I was thinking of staying and continuing the military career. But at the same time, I wanted to study chemistry. There was the aspect of being able to earn money immediately in the military versus self-financing my studies. It was an emotionally turbulent time for me. After fourteen months in the military, my superior gave me his diary. It was horrible to read what he had been through. He didn't think I could live with it, so he asked me, 'If all this happens to you, can you go home and keep playing with your kids?' I was really glad I took that to heart. I dropped out. I'm so grateful to him for sharing that with me."

Maximilian began studying chemistry at Ulm University in Germany. *"I thought that I could finally do my service to the world. Leave the world a little bit better than you found it. That would be my goal in life. You don't have to solve the big questions of life. You just have to do a few good little things. And I thought chemistry could give me the opportunity to do that. I always assumed I would end up in organic chemistry and medical science or drug discovery."* Yet eventually he didn't. *"I totally flunked my first organic chemistry exams. Organic chemistry had always been very appealing to me, but I was too tired to learn all those reactions. It was like memorizing a phone book. I forced myself through organic chemistry. When I did an internship with a professor for my bachelor's degree, he literally asked me to do him a favor and not take organic chemistry in my master's."* Maximilian laughs, but with a certain seriousness he proceeds, *"I actually ended up stepping up my organic chemistry studies for my master's sitting in the front row of this professor's class. I'm too stubborn for that kind of thing. If someone tells me it can't be done, I figure out a way to do it."* That's a useful quality for his startup now.

During his master's degree in chemistry, Maximilian finally discovered his passion for electrochemistry. He describes it as the perfect synergy between chemistry and physics. He earned his PhD in electrochemistry with a focus on battery technology and completed his doctorate in June 2020, about a year before we conduct this interview.

When Maximilian elaborates about what has happened since then, it sounds like he is talking about years and years of work. *"Sometimes it feels like it's been several years, but it's really only been a few months. You get so much more out of life when there's so much going on all day. I love taking things to the extreme and being active. A life lived like that feels like ten lives. Don't stand still, otherwise you'll fall asleep. Don't stand still or others will overtake you. I feel if I'm not active all the time, I'm missing out."*

"Already in the first year of my doctoral studies I realized that I wanted to found a company." Together with his colleagues at university, they had this idea and a big vision that they wanted to develop: *"We combine the whole spectrum from quantum mechanical calculations to experimental and we demonstrate that it works all the way from the microscopic atomic level up to the top."* Maximilian's research group at the Ulm University is working on battery technology starting at the atomic level. They are using computer simulations and experiments to understand what each individual atom and molecule is doing in a battery in order to store chemical energy and deliver electricity on demand. It is fascinating to think about these little lithium ions wandering around between the + and –poles of the battery generating the electricity to power an electric car. It is these microscopic effects, how fast and how well these lithium ions can travel, that determine how long you can drive an electric car on a full charge, how long it takes to charge it, how safe it is and how long it will live. It is the chemical compositions of anodes and cathodes, microscopic structures and interfaces between molecules and metals that power our electric cars. A fascinating playground for a chemist like Maximilian or a physicist like me.

Maximilian realized that upscaling this scientific work would not be possible in a purely academic environment. There was neither enough money, nor enough manpower. *"We needed to start a business. We started using Business CANVAS and all kinds of startup techniques to get going. Our original idea changed ten times. We invested two years to think and formulate what we actually wanted to achieve, and another year to figure out how to make it happen. During our doctoral studies, we met every other month, discussed issues, and took home a few tasks such as market analysis, patent research and more. We never lost our vision: We want to take what we see at the university and what results from the research and anchor it in the industry. We want to work on that with manpower and money. There is so much potential in that!"*

Right now, Maximilian is a postdoctoral researcher at the Ulm University and in the pre-seed stage of founding a startup. Together with his small team, they are currently working on a prototype version of their system and finding funding for their company. He is co-initiator of the project "Zeta Battery Solutions" with the aim to develop an adaptive battery management system to improve battery safety.

The battery management system in a car consists of a little box, connected to temperature and current sensors, and utilizes a powerful algorithm that controls how much energy is going in and out of the battery while driving, charging, and braking. It controls the thermal system of the car to keep the battery in a comfortable temperature range and makes sure we don't overcharge it, nor completely empty it out. It is the system that shows the driver how much SoC or "State-of-Charge" a battery has. It is a value between 0 and 100% and it represents the electric range of the vehicle after a full charge.

In some cases, the battery management system also shows the current SoH or "State of Health". The State of Health is 100% for a new electric vehicle and then decreases according to how you treat the battery in the electric car. At around 70% of the original electrical range of the battery, the battery is claimed to be "dead". Providing these numbers for State of Charge and State of Health might sound easy, but in reality, it is not. And this is why Maximilian and many other companies and startups out there are trying to create the best approach. Zeta Battery Solutions is starting at the atom.

The role of Zeta Battery Solutions is twofold. First, they want to address the challenge of battery lifetime and safety. *"We want to extend the lifetime of batteries. We want to analyze the State of Health of batteries and assign a scientific value to it. This helps optimize the usage of batteries and analyze whether it is better to reuse or recycle. The State of Health of a battery is not clearly defined. I invested hours and days to try to find a standardized definition, but there is none. In physics, everything is defined, but the State of Health of a battery is not defined."* The second role they have with Zeta Battery Solutions is bridging the gap between basic research at universities and real large-scale applications in industry. *"Here at the university, I am working with the team of post-lithium battery technology. These are batteries with chemistries and technologies that use raw materials that are more abundant and sustainable than lithium or cobalt. We are building our system to be ready for any kind of future battery technology."*

"The market is a dream. It has huge growth potential. It has both political and strong social relevance. It is not a niche market. Batteries are used in consumer electronics, in the automotive sector, as stationary energy storage, as well as in the medical sectors. While the economy is wonderful, the technical side is completely out of whack which affects the economy. All the battery companies do what they want. Whoever shouts the loudest is believed to be true. That makes it really difficult on the technical side."

A system like Zeta Battery Solutions could tell drivers of an electric vehicle exactly how damaging their driving and charging behavior is to the battery. *"You want to show a Tesla driver that it is not good if you fast charge your car in thirty minutes because it harms the battery. It will reduce the State of Health of the electric vehicle and you might lose a month of the total lifetime each time you fast charge your car. Am I supposed to tell this to a customer? Who actually SHOULD know about that? It could become problematic."*

"If there was this magic algorithm to control the lifetime on a microscopic level, this know-how could be misused by the market. They could generate batteries that NEED to be replaced every five or ten years, because they want

to sell more. So, we are aware that with our technology we have a certain responsibility to avoid a misuse like that."

Zeta Battery Solutions will be a company with values. *"Profit is not everything for us. The social equality aspect is an ideology we want to stand for. But your bottom line at the end of the year looks different if you throw all your values overboard. We don't want to do that. Does that resonate with investors? It's exciting, but it's also a challenge."*

If a company puts the environmental aspects over purely economic factors, how will they assess the value of a used battery? We have heard different perspectives in the previous chapters, and I think it became clear that the value of a battery during its lifetime is not something that we, and the battery industry, have a clear answer on so far. For some, it might be just a number, a price per kilowatt-hour, but can it be more than that?

What is the value of a used battery?

"First, I consider cost and not value because I am thinking about what is happening with batteries today. Mining cobalt is a problem. So, on the one hand the resources and raw materials are the value. But, on the other hand you could give the battery another value by giving it a second life. There are regions in the world when the day is over, the light is out. If you could do something for batteries that are no longer good in the high-end applications, and instead recycling them directly, we could reuse them and combine them with solar cells and LEDs that can give light. I think that is valuable. But probably today it is not valuable from an economical perspective."

"With our startup we are also looking into chemical processes to enable second life in a new way. Maybe there is a way to chemically refresh a battery again so that it can be used as energy storage in its second life."

"For me, battery value, is a social and political issue. Most of the batteries today come from China. Countries with the right raw materials will get a lot of power. Is such a power shift good or bad? We have seen that those who have

the oil, have the power. Will this be similar with raw materials for batteries? It is super exciting. What engages my mind, is how can I prevent this power shift from going to the expense of humans. It is a double-edged sword."

With his driven personality, critical thinking and optimistic mindset, Maximilian seems to be somebody who never lets anything stand in his way and is always open for a new challenge.

Do you ever doubt yourself?

"There have always been times in my life when things just haven't worked out. In those moments, I'm far from being that energetic and motivated person. I'm my biggest critic. I have always been my biggest critic, and it has been a long road for me to learn what is good and right for me. I have always doubted myself and often stood in my own way. Today, I still doubt everything I do."

Maximilian begins to talk about his struggles to be a family man, his wife's partner, and an entrepreneur all at the same time. He stresses the importance of investing energy in a partnership in addition to parenting his children. He has developed a strategy to better handle situations of doubt and being overwhelmed. *"When I notice my motivation slipping, I take five minutes for myself. I start asking myself, 'What am I doing right? What's working really well right now?' I focus on the things that are good, and that helps me see things that aren't working from a different perspective. Whatever's not working right now, I can tweak it, I can work on it."* That's Maximillian's strategy for protecting and saving himself from a motivational slump and subsequent maelstrom.

What drives you, Maximilian?

"It's a mix. I want to do something that is sustainable. I want to improve things. I want to solve problems for our society. I don't work in a field where I can actively work with people to improve their lives, like my mother would as a social worker or doctors would with their patients. But I hope that I can contribute to making the world a better place. Right now, we're also looking

into medicine to understand how our technology can help there. It would mean a lot to me if our technology could help improve people's quality of life."

"Another aspect that drives me is to start something that then grows. It's just fascinating to me to initiate something that starts to live and grows into the future. But to be frank, there is also an egoistic component. I have certain great desires in my life that I can only realize when I take on a leadership role. I also like myself in the leadership role. So, it's a mix of charity, sustainability, and a little something for myself."

ELECTRIC BUSES
AND PUBLIC TRANSPORT

*It's harder when you come up with a product first and
then try to fit a market, rather than identifying the white space where the
opportunity sits and then building a company around it.*

JOHN WALSH
May 14th, 2021, USA

CHAPTER 09
ELECTRIC BUSES
AND PUBLIC TRANSPORT

I f you know engineers, you are probably aware that sometimes they are very good at developing a solution and then going around and trying to find a problem that it can be applied to. You also probably know that many companies or startups, after an initial bit of success, try to run before they walk.

These are two big learnings John Walsh made in his early years where he often found solutions to problems that did not have market potential. He quickly adapted and changed his mindset. Working for a private equity firm, he found his way into the electric commercial vehicle sector. He quickly recognized the huge market potential and decided to go on his own to make buses and public transportation ready for electrification.

If you happen to look up "Entrepreneur" in a dictionary, you might find John's face. He is a model entrepreneur. His determination to build electric buses drove him to Asia, Europe, and US in order to understand the complete market and this effort was quickly paid off with the largest contract for electric shuttles by a US airport in history. At the top, John has a vision of his company, Endera, to be the first to break the fixed-route mold of the public transportation business model today.

John covers the **Electric Vehicle** and **In-Use** Phase in the battery biography. In contrast to what we have heard so far, he is the first company in this book looking into larger scale, heavier electric vehicles like buses.

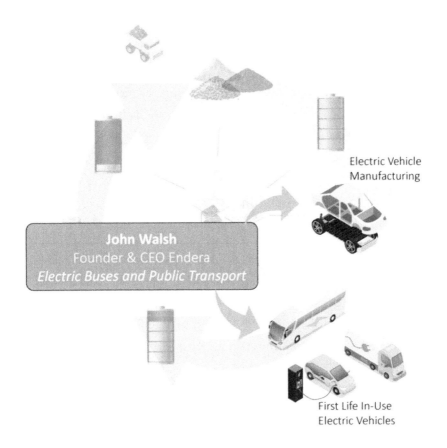

Electric Vehicle
Manufacturing

John Walsh
Founder & CEO Endera
Electric Buses and Public Transport

First Life In-Use
Electric Vehicles

In 6th grade, John read a book that inspired him and shaped the way he viewed his life and his business. I read the same book just last year, right around the time I started my own business. It's a fairly famous book with a counterintuitive story. The author couldn't find a publisher because you weren't supposed to write something like that back then. He self-published it in 1997. Today it has sold 32 million copies in 50 languages. We're talking about "Rich Dad, Poor Dad" by Robert Kiyosaki and Sharon Lechter. It's about how to achieve financial independence by investing in assets rather than liabilities.

John grew up in Redondo Beach, California with a younger sister. He grew up surfing and practicing Brazilian Jiu Jitsu. He has always been passionate about business. *"Ever since I read 'Rich Dad, Poor Dad' in school,*

I wanted to start my own company. That book changed my whole perspective on business. I tried to start my first business when I was very young." In 2012, while he was still in college, he started his first company: Grow Energy. It is a clean tech company that uses a technology to generate electricity by converting algae. For his first startup he assembled a team and raised money. *"I learned how to build a business. I learned a lot - including what not to do."* He smiles. *"It helped me in my other ventures."* Two years later, he started another clean tech company called VENA which involved making water out of air. *"VENA is a water company that uses geothermal energy to condense water from the atmosphere."*

"I have always been passionate about the environment. When I was young, I watched the movie 'An Inconvenient truth'. It opened my eyes about climate change." "An Inconvenient Truth", directed by Davis Guggenheim, is a documentary published in 2006 with the intention of raising public awareness about global warming. It clearly made an impression on John at that time and made him think about using his skills to help make a change. *"I wanted to come up with a product that helped the world but also had a mass adoption."* John is very self-critical and reflective. *"One of the lessons I learned: It's harder when you come up with a product first and then try to fit a market, rather than identifying the white space where the opportunity sits and then building a company around it."* He summarizes his first two clean tech companies as a personal success, a great learning field, but still, *"trying to come up with an idea to fit the market was the wrong way."*

After this first entrepreneurial exploration phase, he went into private equity. He was working at a fund where he was assigned to energy and transportation companies. *"I got signed up with this electric bus company to help them find investors. That was in 2016 and 2017."* John helped them grow their sales pipeline and launch their brand. While he enjoyed the technology and purpose of this electric bus company, his endeavor with them would not last long. *"Companies don't fail because of technology, but because of the human problem: management disfunction and people not getting along because they are not sitting in the same boat rowing together in the same direction.*" He finally decided to leave. "*I resigned and I started my own business the next day.*"

Since August 2018, John Walsh is founder and CEO of Endera. In big letters, Endera's website says: "Transportation Reinvented". Their vision is to create a cleaner and more equitable future for all through best-in-class electric shuttles, paratransit vehicles and school buses.

When John started with Endera, he used his background and knowledge and turned them into practice. "*I went back to the lessons I learned. I didn't come up with an idea to try to fit the market, but I came from the other way looking at the white space, learning about the industry. I observed the uptick in electrification. I had a good relationship with the San Diego International Airport because I did my undergraduate there. They wanted to invest into an all-electric bus fleet for the airport. I thought, let's build it together. I started a consultancy approach. I flew to China, the Midwest and Canada and looked into all the different options for the electric bus. I wrote it all down, presented it to them and made them part of the solution. They gave me a contract, millions of dollars and said: Build it!*" He pauses for a moment and starts laughing: "*It was the largest contract for electric vehicle shuttles by a US airport in history and I didn't have a bus.*"

Well, some people might be alarmed by the magnitude of this situation, but not John. "*I just needed to figure it out. I followed the crawl – walk – run approach.*" This was three years ago, in 2018. The market was not nearly as mature as today in 2021. Not many people were offering or buying electric buses. "*So, I went and built it.*" John first focused on the subcontract manufacturer model, where you design the vehicle yourself while building a network of vendors that work together to build the product and deliver it. This can have the bottleneck of supply chain issues. "*Relying on a supply chain, where everybody has their own interests in mind can be a challenge. Especially in times, when something goes wrong, and they start pointing fingers at each other.* "So, while Endera started out with this subcontractor manufacturer model to be able to deliver first vehicles and scale the company quickly, it eventually became important to control the end-to-end process. They started a vertical integration in the proper areas. "*We had the momentum and knowledge to do that. Too many electric vehicle companies go from 0 to 1000 and never deliver a vehicle. There is a lot to be said about slowly doing things and realizing what you are actually doing. Crawl-walk-run – in that order.*"

"*We raised money originally by the initial business model. We got started, delivered the product, raised capital, and then bought a bus company. Then we stared innovating in other areas where we noticed a white space of opportunity.*" He mentions an interesting example. "*Currently, counting riders and shuttle reports are done by a clicker and someone analyzing this data by hand. We designed a propriety system that uses facial recognition to count the number of unique faces within a bus. It is connected to an app that shows how many seats are available at any given time. It is an automatic process and generates reports.*"

Today, Endera offers electric buses charging infrastructure and fleet maintenance with an energy management platform that tells its customers, for example, when they can charge at the lowest cost. "*We handle the permits and installation, we provide financing to our clients, we offer fleet management. We follow a consultancy approach.*"

Which role does the battery play for your business?

"*It's the most important single component inside the vehicle from a supply chain and control standpoint. The battery is the most expensive part, and we need to ensure that the vehicle is going to drive for its lifespan.*" One of the challenges for a company like Endera, which buys batteries and installs them in its vehicles, is to guarantee the battery for its entire life. As we learned in the previous chapters, batteries age over time, they can fail, and eventually are no longer good enough for use in a vehicle. They can then either be used for secondary applications or recycled. *"We are buying the battery packs with their warranty. We have to make sure that we pick the right battery with the right quality and a continuous supply. In the electric vehicle space, you need strategic partnerships especially with battery suppliers to negotiate an adequate battery supply."* Paul describes the battery supplier as one of the most important relationships in his business. *"It is a lot related to trust and a handshake that you can rely on, just as in olden times."*

"What's beautiful in our space, in the commercial electric vehicle space, is that it is already cheaper to go electric. From a total cost of ownership perspective, it is cheaper and economically more viable to go electric than having a gas-powered bus fleet." The TCO (Total Cost of Ownership) of a bus fleet includes the price of the buses, the charging (respective of fueling for gas powered fleets) of the bus fleet, and the maintenance over the bus's lifetime. Interestingly, as with all electric vehicles, the electric bus TCO improves with increased annual mileage. The more the buses are driven, the lower the TCO of an electric bus fleet compared to a conventional combustion engine powered bus fleet. The most significant key driver for the TCO is the battery. The battery makes up around 20 to 30% of the total electric bus cost in 2021. *"The batteries need to last the lifetime of what's required for it to be cheaper to go electric. For an electric bus fleet, compared to a gas-powered fleet, you have 80% reduction in fuel and maintenance cost, but an increase in capital cost. This higher capital cost needs to be amortized through a lease or financing over the time of 5 to 10 years. This only works if the batteries last this lifetime and don't need to be replaced before then."*

What happens to your batteries when they reach their first end of life?

"Our strategy is that we want the batteries back. They are still 80% usable; not operable for a bus route but they still have 80% of their charge. We can still use them for energy storage and stabilizing the grid with that type of technology." Clearly, John is talking about giving his used bus batteries

a second life. *"We are building a charging network where all our clients can sign up for charging as a service. When the batteries reach their end of life in the buses, we can reuse these batteries and couple them with the charging stations. This way we have an arbitrage with power companies, and we make money from it."*

"The next business model we want to pursue is a battery leasing program, where our customers buy the vehicles from us, and we lease the batteries and take them back." This is the same approach that NIO is pursuing as we found in Angelika's chapter. NIO also successfully implemented the battery swapping business model as a complement to the traditional way of charging, through exchanging batteries in battery swap stations.

In contrast to NIO, from a commercial vehicle perspective, John currently has a different perspective about battery swapping: *"The electric public transportation has been piloted but there is not yet a huge adoption. Right now, our clients are not worried about the traditional way of charging and fast charging, so I don't see interest in battery swapping."*

What's the biggest challenge right now?

"For us at Endera, the supply chain is the biggest challenge right now." If we think about our battery biography, John is far from the original raw material mining as a bus supplier. But he relies on it 100% because the batteries he uses require raw materials like lithium, nickel, and cobalt, depending on the chemistry he uses. *"For us, raw material companies are not an acquisition target right now. We are not like Tesla who is fully into buying mines."* For John, it is important to understand where materials are mined and how that impacts him as an electric bus provider. Endera subscribes to platforms that shows them where raw materials are at all times and where there may be shortages. Endera uses this information to buy raw materials in advance.

"Another challenge is working with and through the government. There is a lot of money available, but they make it very hard to access it and to deal with different regulatory bodies." A third challenge he mentions is education. "We need to educate our clients and politicians about what electric is. There is so much resistance to this transition in our society because people are not informed. Range anxiety is an example. Most people don't understand that by changing their behavior they can adapt to electric driving very easily. But getting people to change their behavior is really hard. We also have a challenge with dealerships. Our teams are doing standardized training sessions for dealerships. It's like a class with an online module, so they learn how to sell electric vehicles." You can imagine that as the author writing this book, I can't agree more with John's statement about education.

Another message that absolutely resonates with me is when John talks about trust and integrity. "Early on, it became important to me, that I want to be a brand that has integrity, that people can trust. We have a lot of electric vehicle companies that overpromise and underdeliver. This was done to the electric vehicle industry between 2010 and 2020. A lot of people were fly-by-nights, got million-dollar checks and disappeared. They stated range and performance capabilities that were not true. It is very rare to have long-term minded people in this industry. Too many are short-term thinkers. As long as they get the contract, they say whatever they want."

"I have a big vision. Endera should be the first to break the fixed route model for public transport." In a traditional public transportation system, every bus has its fixed route and fixed bus stops and a fixed time schedule. "I would like to see that you could get out of the house and request a ride on a bus. You would have a virtual bus stop on your app, so you can walk to it. One of our busses will pick you up. It is a network of a bunch of them that uses an algorithm like Uber. Driver and rider have an app screen that shows the location and time it takes. Then when you get off the bus you have the next micro mobility solution to get to your final destination. Maybe an electric bike or scooter. You have a monthly subscription of say $20 that brings you from A *to B at very low cost and helps the collective good. I want to break the stigma of something that is inconvenient and low class to something fun and environmentally beneficial."*

John, do you ever doubt yourself?

"Yes. I always have those weeks. Startups are interesting. Going from startup to scale is even more interesting. When I first started, I experienced this bipolarity: you are on your top high, but entrepreneurs also fear their company will fail. But the culture and belief you have will get you through it. Just tell yourself, keep going!"

Keep going John, you are amazing and inspiring!

FORMULA E AND CHARGING INFRASTRUCTURE

When I started to really get to know people in the EV industry, I realized that these people are amazing. I just love how super open minded they are. There is this common mindset, a common 'WHY'. I don't see myself going anywhere anytime soon, I love this industry.

STEPHANIE MEDEIROS

May 14th, 2021, Canada

CHAPTER 10
FORMULA E AND CHARGING INFRASTRUCTURE

Have you ever gazed at something amazing, like a jumbo jet or a race car or even the latest home entertainment system, and wondered where it came from? Where is this amazing piece of technology being designed and built? Have you ever realized how amazing engineers are? I have. My husband is an engineer.

Almost everything you use every day has involved engineers in some form, be it electrical engineering, mechanical engineering, or a combination of both. This combination of mechanical and electrical engineering is the catalyst that Stephanie Medeiros has used in her career at ABB. ABB is a technology company that operating mainly in robotics, power, heavy electrical equipment, and automation technology areas. In the area of electrification, the company focuses on charging infrastructure and is involved in electric racing.

Electric racing and charging are a part of the **In-Use** chapter of the battery biography. In comparing the electric vehicles in the consumer and commercial space with electric race cars we face a unique battery lifespan problem. Typically race cars batteries are used only one season. A consumer electric vehicle requires around ten years along with a significantly different demand and drive profile.

Stephanie, who was born and raised in Canada in a Portuguese household, was always taught to do what you want and believe in what you do. She carries this mantra throughout her career and gives it to any student that she mentors to chase their dreams. Stephanie finds herself in a global EV family and enjoys traveling the world working with many other EV enthusiasts using ABB technology to make the world a better place.

Stephanie Medeiros
Global E-Mobility Executive ABB
Formula E and Charging Infrastructure

First Life In-Use
Electric Vehicles

Stephanie grew up in a Portuguese household in Montreal, Canada. The first languages she spoke were Portuguese and French. *"I am both Portuguese and Canadian. I spent many summers in Portugal and still have a lot of family there."* Being the oldest of three sisters, she took over responsibility early on: *"In a Portuguese household, if you're the oldest sister, you are kind of like the second mother in charge. When your mother is not at home, you have to take care of the younger sisters, clean and cook. I had to learn that responsibility at an early age."* Stephanie's family lived in downtown Montreal. Montreal is an island surrounded by the Saint Lawrence River. She remembers a moment when she was ten years old that made an impression on her and gave her a first idea of what she wanted to be: *"I used to see these gigantic ships coming into the port. There was something in my brain that made me think about how big these things are. Who is the person who designed these machines? It was so fascinating that there are people who have so much power to create something so big. I would have the same thoughts looking at planes. They were big engineering beauties to me. I thought it would be pretty cool to do something like that. As I grew up, talking to my family they said, 'Oh well, that's an engineer'. This is how, at an early age, I realized that I wanted to use technology to do something big."*

Stephanie remembers watching the movie Apollo 13 together with one of her sisters, when she was 15 years old. *"We were blown away by this movie. We were so fascinated by space and space exploration. We thought it would be great to work for NASA. Forget that we are Canadian. When we told our parents, they immediately said 'Okay let's take you to NASA'."*

"I am the person I am today because of my parents. They immigrated to Canada from Portugal, and like a lot of people from Europe, they came here with next to nothing. They instilled in me incredible values in terms of work ethic - work super, super hard - but also, choose whatever you want to do. Don't let anyone or anything limit you!" When talking about her family, her tone is very enthusiastic, and at the same time, thankful and humble.

After Stephanie and her sister showed this interest in NASA, that same summer, the whole family made a trip to Cape Canaveral in Florida to visit NASA's Kennedy Space Center. Stephanie describes it as one of the most important and memorable highlights of her life: *"What a crazy experience. There was no launch happening at that time, but just to be there at the launch site and the launch pads, was mind blowing. To see where the Challenger disaster happened. I had goosebumps the whole time I was there. My parents even facilitated some meetings, so we got to speak with the people who were there."*

Neither of their daughters started working for NASA, but those moments shaped their mindset, interest, and personality. *"To me, NASA felt like a huge agency, and I wasn't sure I could make an impact. I was certain I would be working on very important things, but I thought I would rather do it in a different organization. I just felt like I was just going to be a designer for a very long time and not have that position of power. I wanted to start in a different company where I would have a larger impact."* At the time of these deep thoughts, she was only a 15-year-old girl.

With her dream of becoming an engineer to design big machines, she started studying mechanical engineering at the McGill University in Montreal. *"I love mechanical design. It's about learning forces and how things interact with friction. For me, it is easy to visualize having a block on an inclined plane and calculate the forces."* As a math geek, as she refers to herself, she missed the deep mathematical aspects and was hoping to find that elsewhere. *"I switched over to electrical engineering. One of the first classes they teach you is kind of the same thing, but with an electron. So, you have an electron, and you have to calculate the forces and momentum and all this. In my head, it was really hard to imagine. What's an electron? I have never seen an electron. So, I have to say, my brain works really well with mechanical engineering. I had to work harder in electrical engineering."*

As she progressed with her studies, she finally decided to focus on power electronics. *"It was the perfect marriage of electrical and mechanical engineering because you study motors and drives and electrical pumps. It's also about the computer aspects, computer engineering and electrical circuit design. But for me, when I saw motors and drives, I thought, yes this is what I want. And this is what I have been doing throughout my career. And it's fun!"*

Stephanie works for a company called ABB, a Swedish-Swiss multinational corporation headquartered in Zurich, Switzerland. The company manufactures electrical components and offers digital, automation solutions. ABB has been active in the field of electric mobility since 2010. The company provides charging infrastructure for electric cars, electric and hybrid buses, as well as for ships and airplanes. ABB is also title partner of Formula E since 2018. The ABB FIA Formula E World Championship is the electric parallel to Formula 1. Stephanie started working at ABB ten years ago as an engineer and she has pioneered many of ABB's electric activities. Today, she is active internationally as ABB's Global E-Mobility Executive.

Stephanie started looking into the E-mobility space with ABB in 2015. *"In 2015 in Canada, electric vehicle charging in general was just picking up. It was still the beginning of electric cars. I got into it because I was put in place to run the Canadian business for electric vehicle charging for ABB. It was like a startup mode where I was employee number one, and I had a team to grow and execute our activities. It was really fun."* She describes how six years ago, she realized for herself that this electrification market was starting to flourish. *"When I stepped into it, I started to realize that the opportunities out there are massive. They are really big, not just in Canada obviously, but worldwide. When you compare the E-mobility situation in North America and Canada to other parts of the world, like China or Europe, obviously we have some way to go to get to that level. But there is room for improvement, right? And yeah, we are going to get there!"*

According to Stephanie's LinkedIn profile, ABB has sold 400,000 electric vehicle chargers in 85 markets in 2021. *"When we are planning out where to install electric vehicle chargers in cities, the first thing we need to think about is which type of charger do we need. Are we installing fast charging stations with 150 or 350 kilowatts where you can charge your electric car in less than half-an-hour, or maybe a level two charger that is charging your car in about ten hours?"*

Just for comparison, the average household in the US consumes about 30 kilowatt hours per day. That equates to an average consumption of just over 1 kilowatt per hour. If you charge your electric vehicle at a 150 kilowatt fast-charging station, you will use about as much energy as 120 homes. That sounds like a lot, right? It also gives you an understanding of the energy that you are carrying around in a gas tank of a traditionally gas-powered car. With this amount of energy, an electric vehicle plugged into your home can power your home for several days. That shows how powerful a battery in an electric vehicle can be when connected to the electricity grid through vehicle-to-grid solutions.

Planning the right charging infrastructure involves several issues, such as the location of charging stations, the type of charger and the number of electric vehicle chargers at that location. *"In cities, especially in downtown areas, at places with small malls, people won't be there for much longer than an hour, so a level two charger with longer charging times does not make sense there. It's a better idea to install a 50 or 150 kilowatt fast charger. It is these types of decisions that you have to make. These decisions are often an iterative process, where you put a few charging stations in certain locations first, and then as you see more demand, you add more. If you see that a charging station is underutilized, you don't install more."*

Charging infrastructure planning can also be supported by software and simulation, even before the first charging station is installed. It is possible to simulate an electric vehicle fleet all charging at different locations and for different types of charging stations on a virtual map in a fully virtual environment. *"This is what our customers and end users are asking us to see. And it is possible, now that there is software that can do that. We are also collecting data from charging stations to support this process. It is all about big data. Chargers connected to the cloud, so you can get information from them. How often are electric vehicle owners using this charging spot? For how long? How many charging stations are used at a time? Everything is more and more connected, and we learn from this data and information. Like for example digital parking meters. In Montreal, you have an app on your phone that tells you how much longer you can park. This data is very crucial for the city. They learn exactly how long people are staying at coffee shops or malls and this data can be used to define charging concepts. It is all connected."*

In her role with ABB putting charging infrastructure in place, it is important for Stephanie to be part of the whole battery value chain and exchange with other stakeholders of the battery biography. From a charging perspective one of the most important stakeholders for her is the utilities providing electricity to ABB's charging stations. *"Local utilities are really important. When we started with our charging infrastructure back in 2016, when it was right at the beginning of electrification of buses and bus depots, we had the bus fleet operators and end users embarked in the projects, but the utilities were missing. That was a big missing factor for overall success. So, utilities started to make it clear: please involve us from the very beginning."*

She describes in which form utilities are needed in these discussions: *"It's not only about the service itself, for example what rates to charge, but it is the amount of electricity you need from one day to the next. These high-power chargers require huge amounts of electricity and big loads. So having the utilities was really important."*

Other very important stakeholders she mentions are the governments and their policies. *"We need to make sure that with everything we do in the charging area, we are aligned with policies. That's more a national level or even the cities themselves. I was working on a project for electric autonomous shuttles in Quebec and this was a really good example where it was so important to have the government involved because there are different policies that you need to know for different levels of autonomy."*

The last group of stakeholders that is very significant for Stephanie's work is standardization organizations. *"I was part of SAE (Society of Automotive Engineers) meetings about standardizing electric vehicle charging plugs. Standardization is extremely important for charging. Right now, we have two types of charging plugs in North America: CCS and CHAdeMO. In other parts of the world, there are others. We need to limit these different kinds of charging standards, because otherwise it hinders adoption. There are many organizations out there that bring together vehicle manufacturers and charger manufacturers, so the industry is aligned. In these meetings we align and try to agree. That's very important."*

Although all of these technologies around charging infrastructure are exciting for the mass market, with ABB being title partner of Formula E, they are really pushing the technology around electric vehicles to the extreme. Having grown up in Montreal, Stephanie had a connection to the world of race cars from a young age. *"Montreal is a Formula 1 city. So, I grew up with it. People come from all over the world, it's so exciting. I got into Formula E because ABB is Formula E's title partner. ABB was looking for someone to handle the technical aspects of that relationship. That's how I was put in the position. When Formula E knocks on your door, you take it. I'm so glad I did. Part of that role was working with Formula E and FIA to develop the charging for the next generation of car. We started with generation one and are now in generation two of our electric racing cars. There are so many improvements from generation to generation."*

As in traditional Formula 1, the improvements that you see on the racetrack are then taken to the mass market vehicle. *"So, with ABB we are supplying the charging infrastructure for the next generation of electric cars. For me, Formula E is just the perfect marriage of E-mobility and motorsport. It's just fantastic."*

Stephanie gets firsthand insights into which role the battery plays in a high-performance racing application. *"In generation one, the battery was not big enough to complete the entire race of more than 45 minutes on one charge. Drivers needed to switch vehicles halfway through the race. The charging rates were not that fast back then, and they needed to bring two cars for every race and swap the entire vehicle rather. In around a year, we will have generation three and this will be very different. The innovation curve is just crazy. There will be so many improvements. For us at ABB, it is also very interesting for our charging equipment development. We can learn a lot from motorsport charging. The design cycles in Formula E are so fast. You can see improvements on the car, on the hardware and on the software very fast. You then see these technological improvements taken to the mass market vehicles within only two years."*

Stephanie's enthusiasm for the electrification space is contagious. She finds herself in the perfect spot using technology to make the world a better place. *"When I started to really get to know people in the EV industry, I realized that these people are amazing. I just love how super open-minded they are. They are all so excited and so agile and thinking like everybody wants to save the world. There is this common thing, a common 'WHY'. I love working in this industry, because I get the chance to solve a problem using technology, making the world a better place at the same time. I don't see myself going anywhere anytime soon, I love this industry."*

There is no doubt that Stephanie delights in her very exciting environment. And she wants to help others find that place as well. For her it has always been important to give something back to the community.

"When I mentor, one of the first questions I ask is 'What is your wildest dream?' People say, 'I want to work for SpaceX.' Okay, let's make it happen. Why not? Many people have such limiting ideas, or excuses. So, what I love to do is exactly what my parents did for me. Set the stage and work little by little and you'll get there – you'll get there eventually. I have been instilled by my family that you can be whatever you want to be. My parents made sure that we were given all the opportunities."

EFFICIENCY IS THE KEY

When I was having my first baby, I considered changing.
When kids grow up, they start asking questions. Questions that you
sometimes don't have the answer for. Kids make you mad, but they also
make you think in the right direction.

TOM TSOGT

June 8th, 2021, Singapore

CHAPTER 11
EFFICIENCY IS THE KEY

W e've all driven a car before and know how it works. You press the gas pedal to get going, and you press the brake pedal to stop. With a conventional powertrain, you stop by pressing on the brakes. This generates heat directly under the vehicle by the brakes in the wheels. One of the main advantages of electric driving is that when you apply the "brakes", the electric motor can regenerate electricity and charge the battery. The same is true for downhill driving. So, in essence, it's a much more efficient way to capture energy while you slow down.

Tom Tsogt has recognized that efficiency is a key differentiator between various electric drive systems. Tom grew up in Mongolia and spent much of his life running his father's company in the tourism and aviation industry. When he had the pleasure of having his first child, it changed him. When his children grew up and started asking questions, he wanted to have a good answer for them. He decided to change careers. He recognized a challenge in the commercial vehicle sector, as all the dirty diesel vans ended up in developing countries like Mongolia.

Around the time that John Walsh was looking at electric commercial vehicles, Tom came to the same realization. Electrification of the commercial vehicle sector provided an incredible business opportunity and an area to make a difference. He co-founded his company, AVEVAI, a combination of leveraging artificial intelligence, electric vehicle technologies and autonomous driving for the commercial vehicle sector. We can find Tom and AVEVAI in the **Electric Vehicle** chapter of the battery biography, making efficient electric vans and small electric trucks.

Having grown up in the lower middle class, Tom is still grounded (no pun intended) despite his rise to running his own company and has a connection with everyone who wants to exchange ideas. He relies heavily on social media and knowledge sharing to build his network of resources that he can leverage to move his company forward.

Electric Vehicle Manufacturing

Tom Tsogt
Co-Founder AVEVAI
Efficiency is the Key

First Life In-Use
Electric Vehicles

Tom was born in Mongolia in the late 70s. Mongolia is the most sparsely populated sovereign nation and the world's largest landlocked country that does not border a closed sea. In the early 1990s Mongolia conducted its own peaceful democratic revolution. When Tom grew up, Mongolia was a socialist state under the influence of the Soviet Union. Together, with his only sister, they attended a Russian kindergarten and a Russian middle school.

His father worked for a state travel agency and later switched to the private business sector, where he ran the ground handling for private jets coming to Mongolia. *"Mongolia was booming in the mining business. All the executives flew to Mongolia with their private jets."* Watching his father talking to all the *"businessmen with the yellow hair"* in languages he was not familiar with as a child, he wanted to become a translator. *"I thought that was really cool."* When asked if his parents were open to support him to do anything he wanted, he starts smiling and shakes his head a bit: *"I was often the bad guy, because I always needed to try new things. I didn't have many toys. If something was broken, I inspected it myself and repaired it. I didn't have a toy pistol, but my dad made one for me so I could be a gangster."*

When Tom Tsogt was 14 years old, his father was sent to Germany to take care of European travelers who wanted to travel to Mongolia. Tom left Mongolia in 1990 and lived in Berlin for the next thirteen years. Following his dream, Tom started studying linguistics in Germany. But it didn't last long. *"I dropped it and changed to graphical web design and programming. A friend of mine was using Photoshop and showed it to me. I am very interested in learning new things, so I learned it by myself and wanted to do more. My sister also studied in Berlin. She became a bookkeeper."*

Right at the time, while Tom was working for the biggest multimedia agency in Berlin and was fluently speaking three languages including Russian, English, and German, their life in Germany ended abruptly when his mum died in 2003. Tom and his sister went back to Mongolia and Tom took over his father's business. *"I used to love aviation, so I took it over and ran it for the next fifteen years. I changed the company structure and business model. Many Russians, Kazakhs and Americans were coming to Mongolia at that time. It was an easy game for me because I spoke all the relevant languages. I felt confident to take over our family business, because I had worked in Berlin for many years and collected lots of experiences."*

He describes how growing up in Germany for a while instilled eco-friendly values in him. *"In Europe, especially in Germany, you grow up with recycling in your head. Everything must be recycled and reused. You grow up*

120

with this eco mindset." When he returned to Mongolia, he found it difficult to maintain that attitude. Working in the aviation industry with private jets did not support this mindset either. *"When I was having my first baby, I considered changing. When kids grow up, they start asking questions- questions that you sometimes don't have the answer for. Kids make you mad, but they also make you think in the right direction. When I came back to Mongolia, I tried to keep my eco-friendly mindset and I tried to teach this mindset to my kids. When I am 70 years old and the world is not the same, what if they ask: 'Dad, why didn't you do something to change that?' I did not feel good about my kids having a dad that works in the aviation business. Aviation is one of the most polluting businesses, so I investigated options. I needed to find something cool. I looked at commercial vehicles. All of them are diesel vans, which spread around the world, from eastern Europe to Russia and finally they end up in Mongolia. So, we have all these bad diesel vans in Mongolia. I decided to make commercial vehicles that are efficient."*

Tom's adventure trying to find an efficient technology for electric commercial vehicles started in 2016. Together with his family, he moved to Singapore and founded the startup AVEIVA with his longtime friend Argun Boldkhet. AVEVAI or AV.EV.AI is combining the first letters of the words: autonomous vehicle, electric vehicle, and artificial intelligence. AVEVAI is producing efficient light commercial electric vehicles, such as electric vans and small trucks, with a very innovative energy management technology. They are using a supercapacitor in conjunction with batteries to increase the overall electric vehicle efficiency. A supercapacitor is like a high-performance battery but constructed differently and with different materials. Batteries and supercapacitors are similar but have different strengths and weaknesses which are explained later.

"When I started in 2016, I had never done electric vehicles before. I was a nobody in that field when I started. I had so many questions. Nobody paid attention to me. I started studying the market and all the vehicles. In 2017, there were only a few models in the commercial area, but electric vehicles in

*general were booming in Asia. Renault had an electric commercial vehicle,
Iveco, and Mercedes Benz. I started travelling to China and meeting all the
big commercial electric vehicle manufacturers. I talked to them and learned
from them."*

As we read in a previous chapter, this was right at the time when John
Walsh toured through China to find the right option for the electric bus
fleet he had promised to the San Diego International Airport. Tom
explains: *"We thought, the best thing would be to follow the NIO routes. NIO
was clever. NIO had their own money to invest, just like Tesla did. Then, they
built the electric vehicles and after that they raised money from local investors
and made contract manufacturing. NIO could spend 80% of their money in
marketing only. This is how they got all the exposure. We thought we could do
the same with Chinese vehicle manufacturers on the commercial side. We
traveled a lot and met people. We really had challenges finding components,
like batteries and electric motors. We were a small startup with a website with
some renders, but we did not have a product yet. Touring through Asia, we
either got a 'No' or an unreasonable price."*

*"We were so lucky when we found Foton, which is the commercial vehicle
manufacturer for Mercedes Benz in China. We targeted them and after almost
two years of hard work, Foton signed an agreement with us. In their entire
history they had never signed a contract with a startup. We were the first ones.
Once you sign such an agreement you have access to the whole supply chain.
Battery and electric motor problems are gone because you are part of this supply
chain."* With the support of Foton, AVEVAI developed the powertrain of
their electric vans and small electric trucks.

But the real innovation of the overall system lies in the way energy
usage is optimized.

In his research and investigations Tom identified the energy efficiency
of electric vehicles as the key enabler to increase electric range, make
batteries smaller and last longer. *"The energy management system is key to*

the electric vehicle technology. It is the heart of the battery itself." What Tom describes as the energy management system being the heart of the battery, is the battery management system that we talked about in Maximilian's chapter plus all the other control units for the car. Tom recognizes the potential to make electric vehicles more efficient by harnessing the full potential of regenerative braking.

As you drive, the energy from the battery is used to power the electric motor, which is connected to the axles and drives the wheels. When you step on the brake pedals or drive downhill in an electric vehicle, the electric motor regenerates that energy. This is called regenerative braking. The electric motor reverses the process and returns this energy to the battery to recharge it. Various automakers offer different driving modes that use regenerative charging.

Tom and AVEVAI are taking this concept to the extreme and exploiting its full potential. *"Batteries can't take the full load coming from regenerative braking. So, we came up with a supercapacitor technology complementing the battery system together. All that is controlled by an algorithm that decides when this additional energy is sent to the motor or the battery or the supercapacitor."*

Compared to a lithium-ion battery, a supercapacitor can accept energy much faster and can have a higher density. On the other hand, a supercapacitor can't hold energy for a long time, which is why they are not used as the main energy storage system in electric cars or consumer electronics. Batteries are better for long-term power storage needs, while supercapacitors can accept and deliver a big amount of energy in a short time. That might be a good synergy for an electric car.

"When we started AVEVAI, a friend told me about a company with a special technology: a smart energy management system that has been in R&D phase since 2009. We did a test program together with the founders of the company to test the technology. It worked out well and we started a cooperation

to develop this system further. We launched our vans with the supercapacitor system at the Guangzhou auto show in 2018."

"The energy management system is basically a hardware box with software inside. Depending on the van size, we have one battery pack and maybe two rows of supercapacitors. Every capacitor will be connected to the battery management system. A smart and fast algorithm decides, at any given time, how to use the energy in the most effective way."

With this special energy management system and an electric powertrain enhanced by a supercapacitor, AVEVAI has been able to increase the electric range between two charges by up to 40% and the total battery life by 25%. This means batteries can be smaller and vehicles are more efficient and longer lived. *"We have tested and proven this extended electric range with our prototype vehicles on the test tack in Shanghai."*

AVEVAI's technology is very innovative, and they have proven that their concept works. But Tom emphasizes how hard it is to get heard and trusted in today's electric vehicle world: *"I am very open with sharing my ideas. I don't want to hold them to myself. I am supporting E-mobility and clean mobility in general! I am trying to help, but often times I am ignored. I observe other companies, including startups. What are they doing? They use bigger and bigger batteries, but that's totally wrong. These are startups targeting over 300 kilometer electric range with a huge battery pack of over 130 kilowatt-hours. Our van has the same range with an 80 kilowatt-hours battery pack, so a much smaller battery, because the energy is distributed and used in a very efficient way! They could save around 30% of their current battery usage. In the future, when we start comparing EVs versus EVs they will see that there are differences. Efficiency differences of 10, 20, 30%. For some of the manufacturers, it will be too late to change their strategy."*

Tom is in fact one of the most active content contributors in my LinkedIn network. He posts several articles a day and also engages with other people's content.

During COVID, he set a goal to grow his following from 300 to 10,000 people. He wanted to be heard. He wanted to connect with industry experts. Today, he is not only running his company AVEVAI, but also works as an independent E-mobility consultant, sharing his concepts and advising startups and other companies. *"I am a very open-minded person. I am trying to connect the right dots."*

Tom, what drives you?

"I am a family man. Family is everything to me. I like my kids to play around me. I grew up with a younger sister, but I could never ask an older brother for advice or inspiration. I was more or less alone. That's why I love my family. Every laugh from my kids gives me so much energy."

"I hope to have all my answers by the time I am old. I will research and learn until then. With AVEVAI we have failed many times. We failed finding investors. We were talking to the wrong people. We were pitching wrong. But each time I fail, I learn. And I think I can change the view of this technology."

"I don't have a car, I walk. I can't be 100% eco, but I can try."

"Try to listen to people! Try to listen what they really say. No matter if you have time or not. I really try to be a good communicator."

REVERSE BATTERY MANUFACTURING FOR RECYCLING

Our Earth is a sphere, and we all share this planet.
If we bury or burn materials in another place, they will eventually come
back to us through the water, the sea, or the air.
People always forget that.

RUDOLF VON STOKAR
June 22nd, 2021, Germany

CHAPTER 12
REVERSE BATTERY MANUFACTURING FOR RECYCLING

Our planet is round, almost a circle, and like a circle, everything we do comes back to us. So what we do for the environment today with our E-waste comes back to us and our next generations. As you can imagine, this needs to be considered in all aspects of electric vehicle transportation and energy storage. This is the key to the battery biography: "Birth" or making batteries, "Rebirth" by using batteries in a second life and "Reincarnation" by making new batteries from recycled battery material. The better, more efficient, and more complete this process is, the less material we put back into the ground.

As a kid, Rudolf von Stokar was the boy we all knew who tinkered in his garage and fixed bicycles, TVs, and other household appliances. He was the boy we brought things to and who knew how to fix things we couldn't. Soon, Rudolf was offering his services all over the neighborhood. After a successful career in various industries, as with many others in this book, his entrepreneurial spirit took over and he realized he wanted to take charge. He wanted to drive the change that he needed, and wanted, to see. He co-founded Reco-Ewaste, a company focused on recycling electronic goods for the benefit of the future. Reco-Ewaste develops a process which reverse engineers or reverse manufactures used batteries to recover the valuable raw materials.

Rudolf firmly believes that you need to recover almost 100% of the material to make this technology truly green and sustainable. He realizes that the more material you can recover from existing batteries, the less new material you need to mine. As materials become trade goods and are blocked for export from certain countries, one may have to rely on buying used products and recovering them. Rudolf and Reco-E are looking closely at **Recycling** to allow for a full reincarnation of the battery.

Battery Recycling
Life: < 20%

Rudolf von Stokar
CEO Reco-Ewaste
Reverse Battery Manufacturing for Recycling

I was introduced to Rudolf by a mutual acquaintance from Daimler. We had a short phone conversation in which we talked about battery recycling. Even on the phone, I sensed Rudolf's extraordinarily positive and engaged mindset. He told me about a movie he wanted me to watch when we were done. It's called "Welcome to Sodom". It's a documentary that shows how cell phones, LCD TVs, and notebook computers, once they become useless to us, end up in Ghana, where children and teenagers disassemble them surrounded by toxic smoke. *"A clean business for some, toxic routine for others."* Rudolf emphasizes that we simply can't let something like this happen!

A few weeks later, we set up a Zoom call. Rudolf is sitting in his home office since we are in the middle of COVID. He had just founded four other companies. He is very positive, very energetic, like a battery after a super-fast charge. In his background I see a large bookcase. *"I love reading. When I was a kid, I knew the Book Bus by heart. It was an 8-meter-long library on wheels, that came to our neighborhood every week. I was lying in the garden, reading eight books a week. At some point, they were running out of new books. I used to be very interested in ghost stories, but soon it was all about technology and electrical circuits."*

Rudolf grew up in Germany in the late 1970s, in a well-protected parental home, together with three sisters. *"As I have three sisters I know the other side well, too. I've seen everything that men can do wrong to women."* He laughs heartily: *"'You don't do things like that. You don't say things like that.' I learned a lot from them."* Today, Rudolf is surrounded by two girls again. *"I have two daughters and I'm a single dad. They're in the middle of their discovery phase – red and blue hair, long fingernails, and lashes. Recently, they told me to buy Nike Air sneakers as they thought my Hilfiger sneakers were totally uncool. It's very fun to be driven and carried along in their activities."*

"I always had this dream to repair broken things – or improve them – and then resell them. That's kind of what I do today, too. I always wanted to work in sales. People have told me that I can talk really well and tell good stories. I can present a bouquet of flowers to others, so they say, 'Oh, I want that one'."

Rudolf started very young. He remembers how he repaired the family's Christmas cab at the age of seven. When he was ten, he started to take apart radios, remove the transistors, and reinstall them somewhere else. *"I wanted to understand the technology. When I came home from playing football with my friends, I locked myself in my room and worked on these little projects."* When being asked where he got this passion from, he says: *"This was all coming from me."* He admits that his parents must have suffered in part with their son taking the entire house apart. *"I also did it out of necessity. One telephone line and three sisters – so I needed to build a telephone switch box."* At some point neighbors and friends came and brought their broken bicycles or lawn mowers. *"And I got 5 Marks in return. I also started to buy broken cars and fix them."*

Rudolf remembers that school was a means to an end for him. As in many Austrian and German high schools, he had to learn Latin. He quickly realized it wasn't for him: *"What can you do with a dead language?"*

This reminds me of my own eight years of Latin classes, during which we translated literally every war our humanity has ever been involved in into German. Rudolf avoided that and quickly switched to a more technically oriented education. Communications engineering, electrical measurements, metrology. These were the topics he could identify with. *"There, I learned something for my life from people who had worked in the industry themselves. I built a computer from E-waste back then."*

After graduating from this school, Rudolf joined the Bundeswehr (the German armed forces) in the radar systems division. *"I stayed with the Bundeswehr for six years and enjoyed good training, which was also paid for. I took all the courses in electrical engineering. I also got the chance to go to America. With the English I learned there, I came back to Germany and got my first job as CTO of a fax broadcasting company. Being fluent in English was a requirement for that job."*

Since then, Rudolf has worked for many different companies, mostly in business development and sales. From selling chips and sim cards to Chinese and other Asian customers, to building systems to track requirements for companies in the automotive sector, to developing and selling embedded software. Rudolf looks back on a fun, varied and sporadic career driven by his curiosity and business savvy.

131

But his entrepreneurial spirit was too dominant for him to work for anyone else.

"I always wanted to run my own business. I always wanted to do my own thing." Most of the companies Rudolf worked for were regularly bought out by others. He began to think, *"You're putting so much energy into this but you're not getting enough back. You can do better!"* He recalls how one of the companies was sold for $160 million. As a shareholder in the company, he got a piece of the pie, but *"if I owned the company, I would have made a fortune. So, I had this idea that I did not want to work for other people anymore. I wanted to do my own thing."*

Rudolf co-founded Reco four years ago, but the idea was already 25 years old. When he met his co-founders at a conference, their work aligned perfectly with Rudolf's mindset for advancing something important in environmental protection and recycling. *"My co-founders have been busy for ages taking computers apart and determining which metals are in the processors, like 386, 486, 586, I3, I5, I7, Pentiums. There's a lot of gold and other precious metals in those processors. I met the other founders at an automotive convention in 2014, where I was publicly upset that a major German automaker was giving four talks on internal combustion engines and nothing on electric cars. I am well known in the automotive field for being passionate about E-mobility and for working with startups. They asked me to help them found their company which is what we did."*

In 2018, they all went to the notary and founded the company Reco with the aim of advancing the recycling of electronic waste without chemicals or incineration and to extract high-purity and conflict-free raw materials such as silver, platinum, or gold. In late 2018, they expanded this into the founding pool Reco Venture AG, Reco-Ewaste focused on recycling batteries and H2 lab focused on producing green hydrogen.

"We recycle electronic waste, traditionally in the field of computers, laptops and smartphones. I buy E-waste in a sorted and already disassembled state. I

need to pay for this 'high category E-waste'. The better sorted, the more I pay. On the other hand, I get paid for accepting E-waste that is not pre-processed. It is a challenge to find the right balance here." Rudolf explains how they plan to change their business model. *"We are collaborating with programs like 'Anderwerk' that reintegrate the long-term unemployed and also hire physically and mentally disabled to help us with disassembling E-waste. We have already built up a good network that supports us in disassembling computers and laptops to make them ready for our recycling process."*

"We want to recover almost 100% of the materials, and it is possible. It's just a bigger effort and takes a longer time. Most recyclers follow the 20-80 rule. 20% effort and 80% revenue. In the consumer electronics sector, they used to set the E-waste on fire in a blast furnace. The precious metals remain because they don't burn at 1400 degrees Celsius, and then you separate platinum, gold, silver, and copper. The rest is a mixture - a slag that goes to special landfills."

"But there is still lead and mercury in it. You can watch 'Welcome to Sodom' on YouTube. You can see how the earth is moving in these landfills. This is extremely bad for our environment. And it doesn't just affect the people who live there because the earth is a sphere. So, it comes back to us through the groundwater and the fish in the ocean."

"For batteries, there is a big concern about where we get all the lithium or cobalt from, initially. The situation and challenges are similar to how it started out with gold – in black Africa, South America, Chile, and Argentina where the environment and the people are exploited. Nobody seems to care about the health problems of these people and the dust that accumulates in their lungs. They have lungs like coal miners. For mining gold, you extract gold using mercury. These people don't know about mercury poisoning because nobody informs them. The facilities are filled with very young workers. They don't get much older. And if it is not lithium, it is nickel. The same with oil. Combustion engines die because we are running out of oil. Oil will be scarce or 5 euro per liter. The problem is that nobody closes the circle."

Rudolf picks up a periodic table of elements. *"China stopped exporting rare earth materials in 2018. 95% of rare earths are found in China. Yttrium and the rest of the third subgroup in the periodic table are really rare on Earth and only found in a very small quantities and only at certain places. All smartphones use rare earth materials, but no one seems to care. These materials are so rare that it is becoming increasingly important to get these metals back!"*

While Reco traditionally recycles computer scrap and consumer electronics waste, Rudolf wants to specifically address industrial battery recycling with Reco-Ewaste. This includes smaller batteries from E-scooters to large electric vehicle batteries. *"While most electric vehicle battery recyclers want to shred the batteries, we take the same approach as we do with our smaller E-waste. We take the time to disassemble the batteries and reverse the production process until we end up with the raw materials. Our end product is not a black mass, like the conglomerated end product of a typical battery manufacturing process, but we get back all of the lithium, cobalt, copper, plastic and aluminum as pure materials."*

This way recycling turns into a local "mining" opportunity.

Imagine how we could at some point stop mining new raw materials, because we will always get back enough material for a new battery from recycling. It would be a closed loop, a circular economy.

"We can close the circle through recycling. For example, a Tesla battery dies in an electric car. It comes to us, and we extract all the raw materials so they can make a new battery from it. This process can last forever - like a perpetual motion machine. Like the phoenix rising from the ashes in Harry Potter. At Reco, we embrace the "old Greenpeace idea." The earth is finite, and we don't have a second one in our pocket. All resources are finite."

Rudolf receives used electric vehicle batteries from several different sources. *"Some used Tesla batteries are currently supplied to us by workshops or private individuals. There are more and more do-it-yourselfers who replace the battery in their Tesla with a new one to get the original electric range back. So we are getting those batteries. Tesla is too far away to take them back. A Tesla battery consists of around 7% lithium, 20% cobalt, 12% lead and aluminum and copper."*

Similar to Astrid from Saubermacher, Reco had to define their process for preparing batteries for the final recycling step, considering safe transportation, discharging and safety aspects. *"Every battery we receive is checked by us. For safety reasons."* When Rudolf receives battery packs, the first things he makes sure is that the battery is discharged. *"Everyone says they discharged the battery before they deliver it, but we discharge it again. Just to be on the safe side. Even if a small laptop battery that is only half charged makes it into our machines, it can explode due to an internal short circuit. You have to be very careful in a battery recycling plant. Large electric vehicle batteries at 400 Volts and 30% charge could set your entire facility on fire or even kill someone. Lithium-ion batteries are classified as hazardous waste for a reason."*

Battery recyclers are traditionally seen as the end of the supply chain. If we consider batteries being used in electric vehicles in their first life and then as energy storage in their second life, it could take up to 15, 20 or more years before a recycler sees these batteries in their facility. So as a battery recycling company, you have to be future proof with the recycling process you develop today. Will what works today for lithium-ion batteries work in the future for new industrialized battery technology?

Rudolf answers with a clear: *"Yes! Chemistry is my world, and at the end of the day it's just math. You have free electrons, and you have to understand how materials share electrons to bond together. You can use the same information to separate them again. We are very agile with our process. No matter what battery technology comes on the market. Solid-state batteries or others, we can fully recycle them. In electric vehicle batteries, the materials are usually layered and wound, like a large capacitor. It is necessary to separate the layers and coatings from each other. We have the care and diligence to separate these materials in large water tanks and liquid tanks. This process can take up to 10 days. You're like a coin collector with different boxes where the individual elements collect and accumulate."*

Are we in the middle of an electrification boom?

"Until about eight months ago, if you drove an electric car, you were called an exotic. Today, that has changed completely. For me, driving electric only is not the solution either. We need the right technology for every application. Not everyone likes driving electric, we still need gas-powered cars, and I also see a need for hydrogen-powered applications. For electric cars, we need the charging infrastructure. This is what Tesla did. You have to be that entrepreneur like Tesla and build your own network of hotels and restaurants where your customers can charge for free. You eat for one hour and then you can go back driving to Italy with a fully loaded Tesla with all your vacation luggage. In my opinion, the electric car is on the verge of a breakthrough."

Rudolf, do you ever doubt yourself?

"No, I have defined that at the very beginning. There is nothing like impossible. There is a solution for everything. Either you have to read more, and if you break it down to chemistry and mathematics you will be able to understand it. No, I am not doubting myself. I always fell butter side up. When there were times I did not win a project, the next day another door opened, and a new opportunity presented itself. If you knock long enough on a door, it will open – or, you are standing in front of the wrong door. You are juggling with 20 balls at the same time. Some of them fall down, but the right ones are in the air."

CIRCULAR ECONOMY

For me, batteries are the most valuable asset in this energy transition.

PATRICK PETER
April 29th, 2021, Germany

CHAPTER 13
CIRCULAR ECONOMY

As humans, we often think very linearly. And this way of thinking is also found in our consumer goods market. Someone gets the material, someone takes the material and makes a product, they sell it to us, we use it, then we either get rid of it or recycle it, and then it's done. But as you have probably realized in the previous chapters of this book, we have to change our mindset to make electrification successful. We need to think in a circular way.

Patrick Peter, CEO of Circunomics, understands this concept, and his company is focused on introducing this circular methodology to the battery industry.

Similar to the recycling symbol we find on many of our consumer products, Peter envisions an infinity symbol that shows that this commodity, these electronics, or this battery, is part of a circular economy. This will help give consumers confidence that these goods are truly used in a circular economy, and it will make it easy for people to make the right decision. This will also help change the value of used batteries from a dollar per kilowatt-hour to a more environmentally relevant number that indicates what impact that battery has on the planet.

In this chapter about our battery biography, we focus on the **Circular Economy**. We examine how traditionally separate markets, like electricity generation, storage, and transportation, are connected - by a battery. Only if all companies, such as those presented in the last chapters, work together can we unlock this potential. This aspect is very important because it often doesn't get the shine and headlines those other aspects of the battery biography get. This is really a critical component for the longevity and sustainability of this E-transformation.

Patrick Peter
CEO Circunomics
Circular Economy

According to Circunomics, we expect 200 to 300 million electric vehicles in 2030. There could be 400 million tons of used electric vehicle batteries in 2025. And more than 60% of the energy storage demand could be covered by second life supply of used electric vehicle batteries in 2025.

Circunomics is a German startup founded in 2019 by Patrick Peter and his two co-founders. They are neither the battery maker, nor the second use supplier, and also not the battery recycler. They enable a circular economy for batteries. They offer a digital platform to enable this circular economy for batteries by establishing a second life and recycling network. They are the ones that could show where and how many batteries there are at any time. They want to enable that batteries can be handled amongst electric vehicles, energy storage systems and recyclers. They want to track each battery and, depending on its State of Health and market value, decide if these batteries should be still used in electric vehicles, should be handed over to second life energy storage systems or should be recycled. This creates the needed transparency to turn batteries into circular assets.

Patrick was born and raised in Frankfurt, Germany with one younger brother. He stems from two large multi-generational German families with Catholic roots. Our conversation takes place virtually and in German. It is a real pleasure to listen to Patrick. His choice of words is almost literary. He mixes old historical Germanic vocabulary with some newfangled words to create entirely new expressions and phrases that are very entertaining. Unfortunately, much of this is lost in the translation of this conversation into English.

"My parents are from the boomer generation, the strongest birth cohort, where everyone got a job." It was the end of the "economic miracle", the rapid reconstruction and development of the economies of Germany after World War II. Patrick describes his background as one of lower middle class with strong Catholic roots, and very grounded. *"I exhibit a very strict and self-demanding critical work ethic."*

His father also had his own company, so perhaps he was born with a strong entrepreneurial spirit.

Have you always wanted to do your own thing?

"I don't have a straight resume. I've gone through an extreme transformation. I've always been very skeptical of authority. Even as a kindergarten child and later as an athlete and student, I always questioned everything. I wasn't a troublemaker, but I was very rebellious. I didn't just accept what was put in front of me. It was clear to me that at some point I would try to take responsibility for my own actions. It wasn't a scripted path for me, but I think I've always had that entrepreneurial spirit that makes you want to be brave and take a risk when an opportunity presents itself.

Entrepreneurs dare to try. If it doesn't work out, that's not so bad. But if it does work out, you can say, I told you it would work out!"

Originally, Patrick had studied communication science. He describes himself as a creative, intuitive person who likes to work with language. At that time, he didn't feel inclined towards the technical side, but he loved language and communication. After graduating, he initially worked for a large American agency, but at one point it became too boring for him.

"I observed digitalization in many industries and was fascinated by it. But I realized that what I was doing was not bringing me closer to digitalization. I decided to change my education." He began a degree in business mathematics. *"I started something I didn't really think I was capable of doing. It was so different from what I had done before, but also very interesting. In contrast with lots of my colleagues, when I finished my studies, I didn't want to work as an actuary. I wanted to do something with programming and IT."* Patrick started working for automotive clients in the field of digital transformation as a Digital Strategy and Innovation Consultant. *"Well, I finally didn't write a single line of code, but I mastered how to use Power Point. I got a chance to get a really close look at the automotive industry and see where the problems were going to be in the next few years."*

Through his consulting projects, Patrick got the chance to meet certain entrepreneurial spirits who loved to get things done and take risks. *"To me, they were my personal 'real-life' heroes. I fell in love with this topic."* Inspired by this, Patrick co-founded an organization called Company Builder which helps clients in the automotive and digital mobility industries develop new business models. *"Starting a business is almost like getting married. You can't break up so easily when there's a social contract. You have to dare. You have to accept that you can't do it without conflict, even with the most harmonious business partners. Dispute is preprogrammed. Disagreements are part of the game."*

What used to be a project for his customer eventually led him into creating the startup Circunomics. That was two years ago. *"Originally, with this customer, we were only addressing the recycling part. Today, Circunomics closes the circle for industrialized lithium-ion batteries. For every battery, we want to create a "Circular Twin" that captures the entire lifecycle of the battery and digitally maps it on the platform as soon as it leaves the factory. This circular battery twin lives on the platform as long as the real physical battery is in the market."*

Patrick emphasizes that for this system to work, companies and stakeholders will need to collaborate and work together. *"Circular economy only works through collaboration. The market is not yet ready for it, but we observe a mental shift taking place. The market must be built first. A supply chain is linear by default. When you make something circular, you have to rebuild it. We want to make sure that collaboration in the battery industry can be successful. That's why we're building the second-life market and a virtual return network, regardless of where the batteries are."*

"It will be a win-win situation for all market players. The battery manufacturer will gain additional revenue from their battery because it is used in a second life. Energy storage suppliers receive certified second-life batteries and save costs. Recyclers will know in advance when, which and how many batteries will reach them."

As such, Circunomics could help giving the battery a value it deserves. *"The value of a used battery is very dynamic and fluctuating. Ultimately, the battery is an economic good. The market determines its value. From an ideological point of view, I would like to value the battery in terms of its impact on our environment. This is not a number expressed in euros. Used batteries can electrify communities in rural areas. Today, 1.7 billion people still do not have access to electricity. By reusing and recycling batteries, we can avoid extensive additional mining. The battery is the most important asset in the entire energy transition and has a direct impact on profitability, but also on society and our planet. The value of a used battery is always greater than Zero."*

Patrick and Circunomics are addressing a topic that is not so intuitive to understand when you first hear about it, but it could be the game changer. However, with a subject like this it is hard to get the headlines and glamour that the latest battery technology breakthrough gets, or the latest fancy new electric vehicle with solar on the roof. This is why it is even more important to talk about this in this book.

Patrick, do you ever doubt yourself?

"Constantly. Because until it works, everything is kind of against you. We talk to clients and investors who want to minimize risk for themselves. They ask uncomfortable questions and tend to only do things that are close to 100% certain. Nine times out of ten, we hear, 'No, we don't believe in it', 'There are already other solutions', 'The future for this market is too uncertain'. Typically, the world has not waited for you and your team. But you must not give up. You must believe in yourself until the last day. Your belief in yourself should not change with the number of rejections."

"A friend of mine says that your job as a founder is to constantly get shit out of the way. That's your job. On the surface, on the front end, its hopefully good. But, what's behind the scenes, what no one really sees, is sometimes different. There were a couple of months where I was really afraid it wasn't going to work out at all. But I didn't give up." Having gone through some low times, having witnessed what it means to not have enough money at the end of the month, is something that made him keep things in perspective. He mentions this as something that also connects him to his co-founders who have had similar experience in their lives.

Their persistence has paid off. Circunomics is currently ranked as one of the top five startups for the circular economy. Along the way, Patrick has found strategies that kept him motivated and strong. *"I surrounded myself with a positivist mindset and culture. The more positive people you have around you, the shorter the bad times are. The first two years were super difficult because I didn't have a network around me. Getting through the lows* of a founder is all about personality. Are you resilient, are you willing to struggle, and do you have the will to get through it? As time goes on, you get more and more responsibility. You have your first clients. You have employees you're responsible for. You can't just give up."

"At some point, there are so many people involved and the good culture sticks. When you get to that point, it's a success. You're not indispensable anymore. That's the coolest part. You've built something that's self-sustaining and growing."

The growth of Circunomics over the past year has also helped Patrick find a little more time for his family. "Work-life balance is very important to me, but it wasn't always possible. I work less than I did a few years ago, but still a lot and in high density. Starting and growing a business is not always compatible with a balanced family life. You have to be very disciplined. The kids help with that. My son doesn't negotiate, he demands my attention, and the family provides structure. I tell every applicant at their interview that my goal is to be home in time for dinner every night. That's my personal standard, and I want every one of my employees to have that standard. But in general, I'm not this super disciplined person who gets up in the morning and runs 10 kilometers. I'm more the opposite - I'm very opportunistic, sometimes scatterbrained, and unstructured. I start a lot of things. And I have fun."

What is your vision for the future?

"If I think about five years ahead, then hopefully everyone will have an electrified means of transport and home energy storage in their basement. Then I will know that a battery is a product that is part of a circular economy. On each device, you should find an additional symbol, for example, an infinity symbol. Everybody will know that if I return a device with this symbol, it will be either refurbished for reuse or directly recycled."

"You have to make it easy for people to make good decisions. Don't make me think - as soon as I have to think about that kind of decision, I'm likely to *make the wrong decision or not decide at all! It needs to be 'foolproof' and automated. I envision a certain standard process for returning my smartphone. I may even get information about what ultimately happened to it."*

Patrick, too, sometimes finds it hard to make the right decision, a decision that is good for the environment, in a world where it is hard to get trustworthy information about what the "right products" are, and when there is always a cheaper product around the corner. *"Either you don't know enough and do things that are stupid, or you don't have enough money to buy this 100% recycled ocean plastic hoodie manufactured in Patagonia. Or, you don't have enough time and then you fall back to something that you can readily order off the shelf."*

Patrick recalls an example where he was invited to a startup program in Boston, and only after meeting all the other participants did they realize that the majority were from Europe. The subject was sustainability. *"We all wanted to do something good, but in this case we couldn't. At least for the traveling part. This will be better after COVID."*

Patrick is very reflective in our conversation, thinks about his answers before he speaks, and comes across as very trustworthy and honest. When being asked what is challenging him right now, he cites hiring as one of the biggest challenges. He reinforces what almost every thought leader in the book has already mentioned and it shows how this E-transformation is also impacting the job market. Patrick's employee wish list consists of front-end and back-end developers, UX designers, data scientists, and battery experts. A list of expertise we don't have in abundance in traditional automotive companies.

"I have lots of micro challenges. How do I find the right people for my team? How do I keep people happy? Recruiting can be a very time-consuming and lengthy process. Sometimes I have 30-50 interviews for one position. There is a lot of interest, but not many people are willing to work for a startup. What does it mean to work for a startup? I always try to communicate in a

145

transparent way. The information for our investors is also shared with our teams. Everyone knows exactly what is going on. But not everyone wants to know and can handle that knowledge. There are a lot of people who want the security of a fixed job where everything stays the same for the next 10 years. I can understand that, and there's nothing wrong with that, but it's probably not the right mindset to have in a startup. If you want to work in the volatile environment of a startup, you have to have a certain faith in God."

Do YOU have open questions to the battery industry?

"Yes, I have 1000 things that are unknown to me. But, I guess, I often switch into a mode where I want to show sovereignty. In my job, I am constantly talking to people and companies who I need money from. They don't give you money if you don't have answers. You have to be very careful, even with partial questions. If you say, you don't know, they don't gain trust in you. As a mankind we have become more tolerant with mistakes, but still not many people want to see uncertainty or weakness in the working environment."

"If I could ask a battery industry super guru, I would ask: Which technology will be mainstream in ten years? Which distribution do we see in which applications? What is the battery price per kilogram in ten years? Do we hit a plateau, or does it linearly decrease? If I knew where the price will be in ten years, I could buy all the batteries and make a huge business in the future."

Patrick concludes that while the circular economy is the right way to go, we need to build the market first. We don't yet have a market for millions of used batteries because there aren't many old electric vehicles on the road yet. This is a real challenge for the topic to be successful from the beginning: *"You have to convince people that this solution is important and useful without having the big demand for it yet. Especially when talking to investors, sometimes I feel like I'm having a hard time finding the balance between 'Hey, we're saving the world' and 'Yes, of course you will get your big piece of the pie in the future."*

TRANSITIONING FROM ENGINES TO E-MOBILITY

My objective in life is to acquire more knowledge.
I love learning about new technology.

CECILE PERA

May 21st, 2021, France

CHAPTER 14
TRANSITIONING FROM ENGINES TO E-MOBILITY

For over a century now, the workforce in the automotive industry has grown in size to a point where a significant percentage of the working population is somehow involved in the development, manufacturing and use of cars, trucks, buses, and other forms of transportation. There are so many bright minds and hardworking people who rely on this industry to make their daily living.

For most of the time since the automobile was industrialized, it has been powered by an internal combustion engine. This engine uses a fuel, such as gasoline or diesel, to transform chemical energy into mechanical energy to get us where we want to go. Most advances in recent decades have focused on making this engine as efficient and as clean as possible and we've made great strides in this area. This was one of the passions of Cecile Pera, who spent much of her career working to make the combustion process in an engine more efficient through simulations and testing. The "combustion process" is the technical term for the small "explosions" that happen inside the engine when the air and fuel ignite to make the engine run and make the car go. But it also produces emissions which are released into the air from the tailpipe exhaust of the car.

After observing the development of electric vehicles for some years, in 2018, Cecile realized that things were about to change. A new technology was emerging that had the potential to be clean and could, potentially, be run entirely on renewable energy. Electrification. She knew that if she stayed in her current role, she would have a limited working life.

Cecile decided to make a change and started her own company, OROVEL. Having done so, and now focusing heavily on batteries and electric vehicles, she wants to help others to understand the technologies driving the transition from **Engines to E-mobility** and shape their own future in the electrification industry.

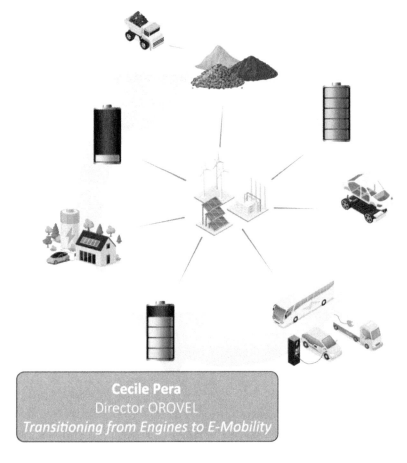

Cecile Pera describes herself as a "content creator for the automotive industry". In 2020, she founded her own company called OROVEL. She is the most active content creator in my network. She not only shares articles and posts from others, but also creates technical substance to inform the market. She covers topics ranging from traditional gas-powered cars to modern technologies such as fuel cells and electric cars. She looks at everything from the microscopic effects of battery anode and cathode materials to the latest technologies in race cars. *"My whole life revolves*

around the automotive industry. I have one childhood friend not working in this industry, but all the other people do. I think there are really cool, skilled, fun, and helpful people in this industry! I love this community."

Cecile grew up in a small village in France near the sea. She describes this region as lower middleclass, but at the same time she recognizes that this fostered her interest in automobiles. *"I became interested in cars at a very early age. As a teenager, I spent a lot of time with my friends repairing their cars and motorcycles in a "do-it-yourself" way. People in that area like to modify and repair their cars themselves. One part because they are passionate, some because it was cheaper. That's how my interest in cars grew."*

Cecile spent a lot of time with her grandparents. *"My grandmother was an inspiration to me. She was very strong in terms of her mentality and her goals in life. She was very active and pushed things forward."* Cecile emphasizes how much her grandparents helped her along the way by instilling in her a very open-minded and free-thinking attitude. *"Growing up, I had no idea that there were things that were just for girls. I grew up very free and natural. I could do anything I wanted. My grandparents supported me in everything I wanted to do. They also helped me pay for my studies."*

Early on, Cecile became interested in science and math. *"I wanted to do something in science because I liked understanding how things work."* One particular moment during her studies inspired her to choose her field. *"There was one teacher who showed us how to use computer simulations like computational fluid dynamics to better understand engines. He was a young professor, so that was very refreshing. I thought, wow, that looks really cool, I want to do that!"*

She applied for his lab and began her academic career in combustion modeling. In 2002, she completed her Master of Science degree at the University of Rouen in France and continued with a PhD in combustion modeling at the National Institute of Applied Sciences in Rouen.

"I got my doctorate because it allowed me to continue doing what I loved. The door was open and there was a lot of light, so I decided to go down that path." In the early 2000s, the industry in France was split between aerospace and automotive. That was when Cecile started to build her network in the latter, working with universities and local automakers, such as Renault or PSA but also international car makers. *"I worked on understanding how the properties of the fuel affect the engine. I've been involved in a lot of projects so there's been a lot of opportunity to develop."* After her PhD Cecile started to work in the industry. *"I much prefer industry over academia. I think academia is a bit distant from business. Academia is slightly too theoretical for me and the politics about publications is so complicated. I thought I would be in a miserable box."*

Over the past 20 years of working in the automotive industry, Cecile had grown her network on LinkedIn to 17,000 followers. *"People are surprised when they hear that I can reach so many people with my posts. In 2020, I had 2.5 million views, and I am aiming for 4 million in 2021."* She compares her visibility to the traditional way of technology marketing. *"Companies pay several thousand euros for half a page in a magazine that nobody reads these days."* What many companies, especially those in the automotive industry, underestimate is the power of marketing through social media and business platforms like LinkedIn.

Cecile recognized this opportunity for herself and turned it into her own business. In 2020, she started her own company, OROVEL, with the main goal of educating the market about automotive technologies. *"I would create content anyway because I love learning new things. Now I can make money doing it."*

What does it mean to be a "content creator"?

"Many companies have good products but don't know how to advertise them and there are people who want to buy good product but don't know how to find them. I create content so they can match. I take content and product

information from companies, such as data sets, pictures and measurements and transform it in a way so I believe it is possible for people to understand. I like helping companies to communicate their technology in a digestible way."

"These days, it's very effective to promote products on LinkedIn. But if you're a small business with only 1,000 followers, it's really hard to reach people. Especially if you have only one product to sell, you can't just keep promoting the same thing all the time. When I tell people that one of my posts has several ten thousand views, they are surprised and get curious."

Before going on her own, Cecile worked for several companies, mainly in the traditional automotive sector with a focus on engine and combustion modeling, both as an engineer and in business development. She describes 2018 as a turning point in the automotive industry. *"I felt a 'game over' moment for the engine coming."* The software she was selling at the time was made for simulating engines and applications in the traditional gasoline-powered world, but not for batteries and electrification. Cecile recognized that a change was happening. She was seeing increasing customer interest in applications like batteries and E-mobility, but in her role, she couldn't meet those needs. She decided to leave that company and start her own. *"This was in 2020, right when the pandemic began."*

"Three years ago, I was still working in the field of internal combustion engines. I anticipated this change in the industry, but admittedly it is even more brutal than I thought. Thanks to an enormous learning effort, 100% of my business today is related to electric vehicles and batteries. My advice to those who have not yet begun to learn about electric vehicles and batteries, it is time to really hurry up. There will be too few jobs in the field of engines in the next few years."

Not only does Cecile help her automotive clients communicate their technology, but she is also very active in sharing content with the public. She also shares content on Instagram and every now and then you'll find videos of her at an automotive event looking for the latest technological trends. All driven by her curiosity.

"The more I learn about batteries, the more interesting I find them. A battery is more than just the cells. People are talking about Tesla Gigafactories, but it is more than that. I like the connections, the safety valves, the vents. I like to see the big picture. I don't think there are a lot of people who have a vision of the whole thing. I'm not specialized, but I'm finding a lot of knowledge as I go into this. I think the battery is one of the most exciting technologies right now."

One of Cecile's unique "creations" are her "OROVEL cards". These technology flash cards give a quick overview of specific types of technology. *"I read 10-20 papers for each of these cards. It is so much work, but I really like doing it."* You can find a variety of collections on her website for topics in the field of engines, business, batteries, and fuel cells. Lately, her interest significantly has grown toward battery topics.

"The battery is also the most challenging component." In the past year there have been several recalls of electric cars due to the risk of batteries catching fire. Almost every major car maker that has their first electric cars on the road, such as Tesla, GM or Hyundai were affected in some way. *"I'm afraid that batteries will have a lot of problems in the future if automakers are not cautious enough. There seem to be some technical challenges. Sooner or later, people will tap you on your shoulder and say, 'Your batteries don't last as long as you claimed.'"*

Do you think we are in a big E-transformation?

"The automotive industry, even the classic internal combustion engine world, has been through lots of crisis. Some people think what is happening right now is a major transformation but for me it's just a wave between a lot of waves. In French we say, 'la vie n'est pas un long fleuve tranquille' which means 'life does not always flow smoothly'. Electric vehicles and batteries are

hyped right now but they will encounter some challenges in the future. Be it supply chain risks, political challenges, or homologation issues. Yes, battery electric vehicles clearly have the potential to help us towards our zero-carbon targets. Nevertheless, I would like everyone to keep in mind that we need to save energy. This means for example go for a walk instead of using your electric vehicle, because driving electric it is not zero-CO2."

"I've asked a lot of people what a car means to them. My grandmother's generation saw cars as freedom- the first time they could drive somewhere. For my parents, a car is needed for work, to get from point A to point B. For a generation like mine, a car is a tool. If you ask the younger generation, it doesn't stand for anything. They don't even care. They just want to chat with friends."

"The problem with the automotive industry is that it has lost its original "raison d'être" - the justification to exist." A transformation happened that is partly driven by E-mobility, but also by digitalization. "It's not just about batteries and electrification - the car became something digital with a screen. The modern car is about electronics and electricity. I think this is what is driving the willingness to go electric. All these new features give the auto industry hope that it will exist in the future as an object that people will want to buy again."

For nearly two years, Cecile has been building her personal and professional brand, OROVEL. She helps people understand what the transition from gas-powered cars to electric cars means by providing information about these technologies. She also lectures at Cranfield University and mentors students. She brings people and technologies together in a unique and authentic way.

"I want to grow myself more than my company." Cecile is somebody who is fueled by learning things. It keeps her motivated. It is her driver. "I always liked to learn new things. That is my personality. I like to learn new complicated or uncomplicated things. I love the moment when I discover something new. That triggers a lot of adrenaline for me." She mentions her unconventional personality as the key for her success as an independent content creator. *"Being free is very important for me. The more I feel constrained, the more difficult it is for me. I know I am different. I am not traditional. My personality is very different, and I like that. With my own company, I can be unconventional. I will do anything to achieve my goals, provided I keep my ethics and what I trust in. I don't like things that are not fair. I can't support injustice. I have no time to waste and do not spend time trying to convince other people. But sometimes being different and unconventional is difficult."*

If you follow Cecile on her social media channels, you will quickly understand that she is not afraid to speak her mind. She's also not afraid to share her feelings. Creating content on a network where there is everything from tradition-minded naysayers to over-motivated hypers can lead to controversy and strong emotions for the person who is in the middle. There is always some resistance to change, and especially in the automotive world. Many people are unsettled about this "Drive to Electric". That's why it's even more important that there are people like Cecile who are educating the world about technology in an independent way.

Did you always want to start your own company?

"I thought about starting my own company for a long time. I thought I would be much older, but many of my friends said: Why not now?" She named her company OROVEL, inspired by her grandmother's name. *"My grandmother's name was Odette Rovel. Honestly, I would not be the person I am today without my grandmother."*

A BATTERY PASSPORT

Sustainability and reducing CO2 are claims in industry.
We are now in a world where claims become irrelevant.
We must have a world where we authenticate claims and
verify them independently. That's the whole genesis.

MATHY STANISLAUS
June 16th, 2021, USA

CHAPTER 15
A BATTERY PASSPORT

What helps you develop trust in a product or brand? Is it based on your personal experience with the product? Do you rely on friends and family? Or on the recommendation of your favorite celebrity? Whether we listen to ourselves, our friends and family, or our favorite "influencer" it ultimately comes down to trusting the products we buy and the companies we buy them from.

So far in this book, we've outlined many parts of the battery's lifespan, which we call the "battery biography", and seen how they relate. We have shown many real-world examples of innovative people working in these different areas. We've also demonstrated how a circular economy is critical to making the long-term prospect of an electric future truly clean.

The people in this book and thousands of others have expansive visions. They want to advance their own technological and business goals, but they need input from each other. Some of them have realized that it would improve their projects and make their lives easier if they had more information about the battery value chain. For example, Astrid wants to know what kind of batteries she gets as a recycler. Darshan needs the historical data of a battery to assess its health. Karin, as a charging provider, needs to talk with the electric vehicle producers and the utilities. Misha wants to have a health card for batteries. Stephanie's charging systems provide usage data. Circunomics maintains a platform for a battery marketplace that can be used by all stakeholders in the value chain.

But for all of this to come together, we need a common system followed by everyone in the battery industry, with defined and verifiable data stored in such a way that the data can live alongside with the battery. One possible solution for this is the **Battery Passport**.

Mathy Stanislaus
Director Public Policy GBA
A Battery Passport

At the time of our interview, Mathy Stanislaus was the director of the Global Battery Alliance (GBA). Shortly before the publication of this book, Mathy took on a new role as Executive Director of "The Environmental Collaboratory" but continues to be associated with the Global Battery Alliance.

The GBA is a growing partnership of around 70 companies, governments, academics, and international organizations. Its vision is to create a sustainable and responsible battery value chain. The GBA's flagship product is the "Battery Passport". Although currently still a concept, the hope is to obtain trusted data and information about each battery throughout its lifecycle. Looking at the complete lifecycle of the battery has inspired the GBA to commit to developing a way to explore the full potential of the circular economy, with a special focus on social and environmental concerns.

These broad social and environmental issues range from child labor, unsafe working conditions, and indigenous rights in battery raw material mining, to carbon footprints, water use, biodiversity loss, and pollution in battery and electric vehicle manufacturing and recycling, to broader economic, technological, and sustainability issues throughout the life of the battery.

Current GBA members typically are mining companies (e.g., Nickel Institute), battery manufacturers (LG, SK Innovation), automotive manufacturers (BMW, Audi, Tesla, VW, Volvo) and battery recyclers (Global Battery Solutions, Umicore) just to mention a few. Basically, every company mentioned that works directly or indirectly with batteries could benefit from such a partnership. Mathy says: *"Currently, the automakers are the most interested in this program. But we see increasing interest from all other players along the value chain."*

Mathy was born in Sri Lanka but grew up in Staten Island, New York, with two siblings and the immigrant experience. He recalls caring about the environment from a young age: *"I grew up in an agricultural family. My father was a farmer. I did a lot of gardening with my father. I started thinking about the environment at a very early age."* Having his roots in Sri Lanka, he was also very involved in human rights. By the age of 19, Mathy was already working for various international non-governmental organizations that dealt with human rights issues. *"When I was growing up, a civil war started in Sri Lanka. That got me involved with a lot of issues, from refugees in the US to human rights issues in Sri Lanka."*

While he initially pursued a technical career with his first degree in chemical engineering, he then switched to law. *"My experience with human rights in the US Congress, and a serious accident at a chemical plant in India that occurred at that time, caused me to change my career path."* Mathy eventually earned a degree in environmental law, which enabled him to link technical issues to human rights at each subsequent career stage. *"I helped organize a coalition in New York City that advocated for environmental restoration in neighborhoods, which helped me lead a statewide coalition for restoration."*

"I received some recognition and eventually served in the Obama administration for eight years. I focused on the automotive sector, which led me to work with the World Economic Forum to build a platform for the circular economy. And today, I'm with the Global Battery Alliance."

What is your role at the Global Battery Alliance?

"The GBA is nascent. The idea is to bring together stakeholders along the battery value chain from the private to the public sector to drive greenhouse gas reduction and promote responsible sourcing. We want to accelerate and drive the diffusion of E-mobility and electrification. I am helping to harmonize perspectives. One of the underestimated challenges is negotiating principles that all the members could agree on. It is very challenging to have this broad spectrum of companies all agree on a common perspective about the topics around circularity, greenhouse gases and responsible sourcing."

After learning about all the different experiences and perspectives in previous chapters, I think it becomes clear that harmonizing everyone's ideas and actions on an international level is a necessary challenge. There are local policies, governmental organizations and cultures with different mindsets affecting the adoption and technological development of electrification. On the technical side, we find a variety of approaches, from creating safer and longer living batteries, to making batteries smaller, through charging them from the road, to exchanging batteries in swapping stations, or combining batteries with supercapacitors and designing them for reusability and recyclability.

Mathy emphasizes how important it is to create transparency. Creating transparency to generate trust. *"The world is moving in a direction where with every major product we buy, we want to know how good it really is for our environment. For example, we want to know what the greenhouse gas footprint of a computer is."* First and foremost, we need to build a data infrastructure that allows us to generate and analyze this information. Second, *"We have to be able to trust the results. We can't just slap a label on it. The whole discussion about greenwashing is happening because these representations lack data support."*

"Today, we are in the unique historical situation of not only having the climate crisis, but also having the ability to track data at the point of origin to ensure that this data is immutable as it flows through the ecosystem. The challenge is how can we address the climate problems using this data? We need to take this to the public to have public conversations about it. We need to start a transition by G7 countries agreeing on a set of data rules to create a global framework for data governance for the climate. And for a battery passport."

Are you only focused on the battery or also other technologies?

"Our efforts are focused on the battery value chain. It touches on all materials going into the product but also batteries scaling up for energy storage, E-mobility, and renewable energy. We want to promote energy access in places like Africa and the value of energy storage for energy access while protecting abuses in the battery value chain. The why and what are clear, but the how may be iterative."

"With the Global Battery Alliance, we have committed to authenticated data as the flagship for achieving this goal. We're in the midst; we're the first of its kind in the world to try to establish basic governance rules for data to achieve public outcomes. I had a discussion with the Biden administration. We can talk about the Paris Agreement and all that, but until you authenticate the data, it's all just claims. Similar to responsible procurement or sustainability, all of these things are just assertions. Now we need to

authenticate and independently verify these claims! We now live in a world where these claims are irrelevant. We need to create a world where we authenticate these claims. That's the whole genesis."

A battery passport helps establish a reliable baseline for all phases of the battery biography. From birth to rebirth to reincarnation. *"We need to assign what is the amount of energy used in the battery manufacturing stage. Of that energy input what is the mix of renewable energy and coal and gas."* The same for the production of battery packs from cells, the manufacturing of electric vehicles, as well as the reuse and recycling stages. *"All these things need to be built up into one regular system."*

In this way, the battery passport provides a trustworthy framework for a full lifecycle assessment.

Mathy appreciates the work that various startups are putting into developing data analytics and circular economy platforms and emphasizes that this will be in synergy with the guidelines and the document created by the GBA. *"All these startups are great! We interact with a lot of them. But at the end of the day, the world is suffering not because of the lack of data, but because of the lack of promoted shared data that is interpreted in an INDEPENDENT way. There are a lot of closed data systems out there. Some intra-company systems, some inter-company systems. These are all closed systems based on data rules with an output that no one can trust. It doesn't matter if it's blockchain or an enterprise system or a handheld device, what matters is trusted data, and we need to organize that data and drive independent verification. So that, ultimately, it's trusted data. All these startups and some large IT companies are part of the ecosystem but not socialized to operate. We need to develop their credibility."*

"The GBA is trying to create a sacred space where full disclosure conversations can happen. Looking at our policies, I've had many provocative discussions where it's 'if you ask me to share this, I will leave."

Which battery data do these companies want to protect?

"Call it intellectual property or anti-trust. There are a lot of perceived barriers that people put up without understanding what we are trying to solve with data. I don't need to know the specific composition of a pipe to say I need a pipe that will deliver water. The same is true for the batteries. I notice that there are a lot of uninformed conversations about protected boundaries. Right now, the conversations about data are being had by either legal counsel or senior engineers; from a narrow perspective, where every single piece of data is considered a trade secret. When I compare that to the public commitments of these companies: '0 carbon by date x, responsible sourcing', I observe a big disconnect between internal conversations and external commitments. It takes a CEO, multi government aligned requirements and public pressure to force the need for data rules for those outcomes."

The European battery regulations currently require full disclosure of battery management system data to drive secondary use of electric vehicle batteries. *"This of course led to some sharp reactions from auto makers. But, if we want to enable battery reuse, we need to share data. We need to have an open conversation about what data we need based on specific outcomes such as repurposing of batteries and what data does not need to be shared based on security and intellectual property considerations. We have consulted with reuse and recycling facilities to find out what data they need to do their job. Battery reuse costs can be reduced by 75% if they have a certain amount of data!"*

When being asked if he personally believes in a second life for electric vehicle batteries in energy storage systems, Mathy confirms some of the concerns we have expressed in previous chapters. *"Good question. I think in the near future there will be a business case, but it depends on several factors. There's the standardization of interfaces with grids that needs to be solved. There's also the data issue that needs to be solved. In the next ten years there will be two million tons of used batteries from electric vehicles. Either they will be landfilled, or we will allow the economy to reuse and recycle them. From an environmental perspective, extending the life of batteries to reuse them in a second life energy storage is great. There are projects looking at the possibility of using electric vehicle batteries in places in Africa that don't have access to electricity while ensuring that collection and recycling programs are in place. There are many possibilities, but also many unknowns. There could be batteries designed for storage that are cheaper than reuse."*

Several times in our conversation, Mathy emphasizes that the social risks in the battery industry are not new for these technologies but are challenges that have gone unaddressed in other industries in the past. But he observes a change. He observes that public and political pressure is almost forcing companies to adapt and take these risks seriously.

"The issue of child labor in supply chains is not new. The issue of human rights violations is not new. Historically, the position of the downstream companies has been: 'I put it in my corporate policies and that's where my responsibility ends.' Today, ironically a change is being fueled by the financial system. Black Rock has put some pressure on, some of the institutional investors have put pressure on, and that's because of public and political pressure; some because of consumer pressure, some because of international NGO. You can't say 'it's none of my business' anymore."

Mathy, what drives you?

"I want to create public purpose good outcomes. I want to align diverse perspective and diverse stakeholders for a broad outcome. In my opinion, collaboration is the solution to our future. And this is what truly drives me."

Uniquely combining his strong integrative nature with a technical background, Mathy's primary focus is on the challenge of sharing data to enable an ethical, responsible, sustainable circular economy for batteries. The battery passport, as a tool that allows documentation of the battery biography and participation of all industries involved, is a possible solution to the green promises we so often read about.

"We are on a journey - there will be many slips along the way. But there is no question in my mind that the future depends on what we have started. Whether we are the ones delivering the results or we are laying the foundation, I am okay with either way."

INTERVIEW PARTICIPANTS

Darshan Virupaksha
Co-Founder Nunam

E-Waste & Battery Reuse

Spirit Animal: ***Beaver***

"I am a beaver.
It uses local resources to create an
opportunity for himself."

Donald Sadoway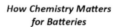
Prof. MIT, Co-Founder Ambri

***How Chemistry Matters
for Batteries***

Spirit Animal: ***Cat***

"I would choose the cat. The cat is
independent, silent, mysterious,
elegant, very much attuned to its
surroundings."

Angelika Berger-Sodian
CEO Europe MOOV

Electric Cars & their Multi-Use

Spirit Animal: ***Tiger***

"The tiger is an energetic and
powerful animal. Once in action,
the tiger has an impact but is very
agile and adaptable."

Paul Beach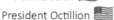
President Octillion

The Third Wave of Electrification

Spirit Animal: ***Black Bear***

"I would joke and say Manatee but
I guess I'll go with a black bear. I am
from Maine."

168

Karin Ebbinghaus 🇩🇰

CEO Elonroad 🇩🇰

Charging Electric Vehicles from the Road

Spirit Animal: **Airedale Terrier**

"I am an Airedale terrier like my dog. They are not so well behaved, very stubborn, they do what they like to do and not what they are told to do."

Mikhail Slepchenkov 🇧🇬

Engineering Director TAE 🇺🇸

Electricity Generation

Spirit Animal: **Dolphin**

"I love dolphins. I was thinking one day that in my next life if I have to be an animal, I would love to be a dolphin."

Astrid Arnberger 🇮🇹

Head of R&D Saubermacher 🇮🇹

Battery Recycling

Spirit Animal: **Cat**

"I would be a cat because it is stubborn and has its own will."

Maximilian Ceblin 🇩🇪

Co-Founder Zeta Battery 🇩🇪

Managing Batteries Starting at the Atom

Spirit Animal: **Owl**

"I am an owl. I often get the feedback to act observant first until I see my chance and then I become very active. And it goes well with my night activity."

John Walsh

Founder & CEO Endera

Electric Buses and Public Transport

Spirit Animal: **Chameleon**

"I am a Chameleon. You have to adapt to different situations to get what you want."

Stephanie Medeiros

Global E-Mobility Executive ABB

Formula E and Charging Infrastructure

Spirit Animal: **Sloth**

"I used to be an energizer bunny. Through meditation, I've learned to slow things down, be more in the present, and have become even more productive as a result. So today I am attracted to a sloth."

Tom Tsogt

Co-Founder AVEVAI

Efficiency is the Key

Spirit Animal: **Lion**

"A lion.
They rule a whole pack, and they die somewhere alone."

Rudolf von Stokar

CEO Reco-Ewaste

Battery Reverse Manufacturing for Recycling

Spirit Animal: **Lion**

"My little daughter assigned me a lion. I would have chosen a dragon. They can be friendly like Grisu, but also evil. The same goes for a lion."

170

Patrick Peter

Co-Founder Circunomics

Circular Economy

Spirit Animal: **Octopus**

"Octopus. Eight tentacles that can all 'think' and act more or less independently. That's handy when you have your hands full. Plus of course the camouflage feature and flexibility."

Cecile Pera

Director OROVEL

Transitioning from Engines to E-Mobility

Spirit Animal: **Koala Bear**

"Koala bears are my favorite animals. I love them. They are really cute but in fact they can be seen fighting each other."

Mathy Stanislaus

Director Public Policy GBA

A Battery Passport

Spirit Animal: **Bear**

"I would be a bear, because a bear would focus on the collective good."

Animal Artwork by Ferdinand Obersteiner

ACKNOWLEDGMENTS

First and foremost, I want to thank all the inspiring thought leaders who took the time to share their amazing stories with me. Stories that were told not only from a professional perspective, but also from a personal one. After each conversation, I was filled with joy and excitement to be part of this amazing movement. And I was sure that many people out there would find some inspiration and clarification through these life stories.

If there is anything you would like to know more about, please contact me through any of my professional or social media channels.

Second, I would like to thank my younger brother, Ferdinand Obersteiner, for drawing the little "spirit animals" that are printed in the previous section. It was fun to discuss these spirit animals with each person and understand how it reflects their personalities.

Third, I want to thank Claudia Stroud and Carolyn Hall sincerely and wholeheartedly for their advice and expertise in helping me make this book something I am proud of and eager to share with others. In a very short time, they not only pointed me in the right direction, but also gave me exactly the knowledge I needed to turn my writing into a real book.

Finally, I have to thank my soulmate, Don, for putting up with me over the last few months while I wrote this book, and for giving me lots of great ideas and helping me put it all together. He had no hair before and now he has even less. But seriously, it's been a great experience working with him on our very first book, and we've both developed a new appreciation for the writers and authors out there - and for their spouses.

In closing, I would like to thank everyone who has read this book. I hope this book was interesting, exciting, or sparked your passion to take action and pursue your dreams for whatever inspires you. And if you have been inspired by this E-transformation movement, please share this book with others, because we are all a part of making this "Drive to Electric" successful.

ABOUT THE AUTHOR

D r. Veronika Wright is an electrification enthusiast, consultant, and author. She holds a PhD in Technical Physics from the Graz University of Technology in Austria and gained extensive industry experience in batteries and electrification before founding her own social enterprise, *Electrified Veronika*, in 2021. With a passion for people and technology, she provides education, technical and business consulting, as well as mentoring in battery lifecycle management for clean transportation and energy. Having grown up in Austria and now living in the US, she lives by the mantra, "it is 100% impossible if you don't try," and is passionate about sharing this global perspective on the world's "*Drive to Electric*".

Dr. Wright lives with her husband, Don, in Franklin, Wisconsin. You can find her online at www.electrifiedveronika.com.

Printed in Great Britain
by Amazon

84585313R00102